M000105716

Gifted Girls®

Activities Guide for 365 Days of the Year!

Fun Things to Do for Kids and Grown-ups that'll help Develop Creativity, Social Skills, and Self-Confidence!

By

Kailin Gow

Published by Sparklesoup Studios, Inc.
Copyright © 2003 by Kailin Gow
All Rights Reserved. No part of this book may be repro-
duced or transmitted in any form or by any means, graphic,
electronic, or mechanical, including photocopying, record-
ing, taping or by any information storage or retrieval sys-
tem, without the permission in writing from the publisher
except in case of brief quotations embodied in critical arti-
cles and reviews.

Published by Sparklesoup Studios
For information, please contact:
Sparklesoup Studios, Inc.
P.O. Box 2285
Frisco, TX 75034

First Edition.
Printed in the United States of America.
"Gifted Girls"® is a registered trademark of Sparklesoup
Studios, Inc.

Library of Congress Cataloging-in-Publication Data
Gow, Kailin, 1970-
Gifted Girls® Activities Guide for 365 Days of the Year:
Fun Things to Do for Kids and Grown-ups that'll Help
Develop Creativity, Social Skills, and Self-Confidence/
by Kailin Gow
p. cm. - (Gifted Girls Series)
Summary: Want to know what to do any day of the year,
whether you're by yourself or with a group? With this
guide to activities for every day of the year, you will
never be bored!

ISBN: 0-9714776-1-2
Activities – How-To – Non-Fiction.
[1. Activities - Non-Fiction. 2. Self-Development – Non-
Fiction. 3. Games – Non-Fiction.]

This book is dedicated to my Mom, Lucy, who managed to raise my brother, myself, and our cousins Victor and Charlie with as much creativity and sense of community as a busy woman and mother could. It is through her dedication to us as a mother that we are who we are today. Her love for learning and her zeal for teaching, as an elementary teacher by profession, has encouraged me to do the same through writing.

Introduction

The Gifted Girls® Activities Guide for 365 Days of the Year: Fun Things to Do for Kids and Grown-ups that'll Help Develop Creativity, Social Skills, and Self-Confidence is based on the fiction series called The Gifted Girls® - the adventures of ordinary girls with extraordinary gifts and talents.

Many of the activities selected for this book are designed to use and develop different elements of social and creative skills. Although many activities can be performed by children as young as 7 years old and up, adult supervision or participation of all activities is strongly recommended.

So, put on your best "can-do, let's have fun" attitude, and let's get started!

Meet Your Guides

Starting a new project can be scary, but is always exciting. You are not alone, though. To help you off to a great start with the activities in this book, the girls from the Gifted Girls Series of books will be your guides throughout. After all, these girls contributed to the making of this guide by including the activities they're especially good at. So, put away your fears, grab some friends and family, and go have fun!

Meet your guides:

Lucy – She is a Gifted Girl living in modern times who is gifted in sewing and crafts.

Emily – She is a Gifted Girl living in turn-of-the–twentieth century England who is gifted in painting and the arts.

Jackie – She is a Gifted Girl living in 1970s America. She loves anything to do with nature, science, and animals. Her gift is the ability to communicate with animals and to understand nature and science.

Daniella – She is a Gifted Girl living in a timeless France. Her gift is cooking and baking.

Rose – She is a Gifted Girl living in 1930s America. Her gift is performing – singing, dancing, acting, writing, and playing musical instruments.

These Gifted Girls use their magical gifts to help others around them, but they also know how to have fun, explore their world, play games, and do activities that help them understand themselves and other people better. Step into their shoes with these activities each day, and you'll see that in your own way, you are doing something wonderful, too. Best of all, you do not need any magic to perform any of the activities in this book. Or do you? Have fun!

Kailin Gow otherwise known as Victoria London,
Creator and Author of the Gifted Girls Series

Welcome to 365 Days of Activities!

There are "sew" many activities
and ideas here!
Note: When performing any of
these activities . . . don't rush it.
Just take it one day at a time.

Day 1
Make a Ribbon Bookmark

Directions: Find an assortment of ribbons and cut a 7" piece from each. Use this 7" ribbon as a new bookmark.

Day 2
Try Hot Chocolate in Different Flavors

Day 3
Make a Wall Mural

Materials:
Large roll of paper, or several large sheets of paper taped together.
Paints, markers, or crayons

Directions: Get permission from an adult before you tape or pin paper to one of your walls. Cover the floor, bed, or whatever else below with newspapers or a drop cloth (old sheet is fine). Sketch the picture in pencil first on the paper. Then paint the mural. If you are working with a friend or family member on this, divide the mural up and paint certain parts of it together.

Day 4
Stained Glass Collages

Materials:
White drawing paper
Newspaper
Waxed paper
Book-dried flowers
Crayons
Pencil or crayon sharpener
Glitter (at hobby or art supply stores)
Iron

Directions: Place a sheet of drawing paper on top of a piece of newspaper. Place a sheet of waxed paper on top of the drawing paper. Arrange book-dried flowers on the waxed paper. Remove the protective paper covering from old crayons and sharpen them over the flowers. Let the shavings fall evenly over the flowers. Scatter glitter over the flowers and shavings. Place a second sheet of waxed paper over the flowers and the decorations. Have an adult seal the two sheets together with an iron set at a low temperature. "Hang" the collage in a bright window with tape.

Day 5
Find a Pen Pal from another Country and Write

Ask your teacher about possible pen pal programs with a school from another country.

Day 6
Crayonful Place Holder

Materials:
Assorted crayons (about 5 or 6)
Ribbon or String

Directions: Tie the crayons together in a bundle with the ribbon or string. Arrange them so the crayons could stand up. Write your party guest's name on an index card and place the card securely in the crayon place holder. Set on the table.

Day 7
Make a Winter Wreath

Day 8
Write a Winter Play with Your Friends

Day 9

Game of Elimination

Can be played with 6 or more Players

First, a piece of paper is torn into as many pieces as there are players: one piece is marked with an X and all the pieces are folded in half. Mix the scraps up and distribute one to each player. Everyone now peeks at their own scrap, without showing anyone else. The player with the paper with the X is the secret "assassin." The object of the game for the one chosen as the assassin is to "kill" off the other players, which he does by slyly winking at them, one at a time. For the other players, the object is to catch the eliminator in the act of winking at another player, before being winked at themselves. As the players look at each other's faces in search of the assassin, the eliminator tries to catch the eye of one person – his victim. When a player is winked at, she must wait 10 seconds, then say, I'm dead," and then drop out of the game. The eliminator tries to kill off as many players as possible before getting caught. If someone thinks she knows who the killer is, she may make an accusation. If she is right, she wins the game; if not, she's out of the game. If no one discovers his identity, then the assassin wins.

Day 10

Go Ice-Skating

Day 11

Visit an Animal Shelter with Your Parents

Day 12

Make a Satin Wreath

Materials: 1/2 yard green satin
16 ounces polyester fiberfill
ribbon cut in assorted colors, widths, and lengths.

Directions: Cut three 5x42-inch strips of green satin. Fold each strip in half lengthwise (with right sides facing); pin the two sides together. Sew top and side seams together, leaving bottom edge open. Turn right side out and stuff; slip-stitch opening.

Tack the three pieces together at one end; begin braiding. Shape braid into a circle; stitch ends together securely. Tie a large bow, using several lengths of ribbon to hide the joined ends.

Day 13
Hug each other

Create a tradition where you hug each other every day!

Day 14
Have a Pal of the Day

Materials:
Butcher paper, crayons.

Directions: Choose someone from your family or group of friends as the special pal of the day by drawing their name out of a hat.

Make a special "portrait" of the pal by having the chosen person lie down on a big piece of paper. Then outline her body on the paper and color it in with the rest of your family or friends. Everyone gets to write something friendly on the paper before presenting it to the chosen person.

The pal of the day will get to do anything she or he wants to do in the day such as eat ice cream, play video games, go to the zoo, or watch movies.

Choose a pal of the day once a week or month!

Day 15
Make Some Fruit Jam

Ingredients:
1 cup cold water,
2 envelopes unflavored gelatin,
2 pints fresh sliced strawberries, raspberries, boysenberries or a combination.

1/2 cup sugar (if fruits are more ripe, then less sugar.)
1/4 cup lemon juice

Directions: Wash the fruit, pulling off the stems and leaf tops. Slice the fruit using a plastic knife. Take out the mushy fruit and gently rinse the fruit in a colander. Add the fruit, sugar, and lemon juice to the pan. Bring to a boil, then simmer for 10 minutes, stirring occasionally and crushing the fruit slightly. Spoon into jars; cool slightly before refrigerating. Chill until set, about 3 hours. Store up to 4 weeks in the refrigerator or up to 1 year in the freezer.

Day 16
Write your own lyrics to a popular song

Day 17
Create a Night Light

Make an attractive tin can lantern for your room or as a gift

Materials:
Empty metal food can (label should be removable).
Permanent marker
Assorted nails
Hammer
Towel

Directions: Remove the label from the can by running it under warm water and then scraping off the remainder. Draw a pattern of dots on the outside of the can with the permanent marker (let the ink dry). You can draw butterflies, rainbows, geometric shapes, stars, moons, people, anything you can think of! Fill the can with water and place in freezer. Leave for at least 24 hours in order to freeze solid. This will keep the can's surface solid enough to hammer through. Place the can on its side on a folded towel. Have an adult use the assorted nails to pierce through the pattern of dots you've drawn. The adult shouls hammer the nails in just far enough to piece the metal. If the ice starts melting too quickly, return the can to the freezer for a few hours. When done, place in the sink and let the ice melt. Dry the lantern and place a small candle in it. Be careful not to scratch yourself on the inside of the can. Be sure to light the candle only with an adult's permission.

Day 18

Melon Dessert from Israel

Ingredients:
2 small cantaloupes
4 peaches
1/2 pound green grapes
1 teaspoon cinnamon
1/2 pound red grapes
1 cup white grape juice

Directions: Have an adult cut melons in half. Scrape out and discard seeds. With a melon baler, cut melon flesh into small balls, or cut it into small pieces with a sharp knife, being careful not to pierce the skin. Wash grapes and remove from stems. Discard any seeds in grapes. ·Save 4 to 5 tiny clusters of red grapes for decoration.

Have an adult half fill a medium saucepan with water and bring to a boil over high heat. The adult should carefully place peaches into boiling water. After 5 minutes, remove them with a slotted spoon. When peaches are cool enough to handle, peel and cut into small pieces. In a large bowl, combine cinnamon, grape juice, melon, grapes, and peaches, and stir. Spoon mixture into melon shells. Top with reserved grape clusters. Refrigerate and serve cold.

Day 19

Have a Sweatshirt Decorating Party with Your Friends

Day 20

Know How You Look to Others

Material: Large mirror

Directions: Look in the mirror. You can do this with your parent, friend, or sibling. Practice different faces in the mirror together. Look frightened, disgusted, angry, worried, and surprised. Notice how this makes your face look. Now look at yourself in the mirror. Smile with sincerity, as if you really really love this person you see in the mirror. Openly give yourself this love. Notice how wonderful you look! Others will see how wonderful you look too!

Day 21

Fly a Fish Kite

Material:
White fabric, about 16" x 24"
Acrylic paints
Brush
Plastic lid from a coffee can
Scissors
Needle and thread
String

Directions: Fold the fabric in half lengthwise and draw the shape of a fish on it. Place the bottom of the fish on the fold of the fabric. Make sure the fish's mouth measures 4 1/2", so that it will fit snuggly around the coffee can lid when it's sewn. Cut along the outline. Open up the fabric, and place it on some newspaper. Paint the fish with acrylic paints so that both sides match. Let the paint dry. Poke a hole in the center of the coffee can lid with the scissors and cut out the entire center, leaving just the rim. Fold the fish along the center fold, right sides together, and stitch the long edge with small, even stitches. Place the lid rim around the fish's mouth and fold about an inch of fabric over the rim, concealing it. Stitch the fabric in place. Turn the fish right side out. Cut a piece of string about 20" long. Poke two small holes in the fabric on opposite sides of the mouth and tie the string to the rim. Tie another, longer string to the middle of the first one. Lash the wind sock to a pole or porch railing, so it is blown horizontally when there's a breeze.

Day 22

Make a Photo Wrapping Paper

Directions: Photocopy your photos and use as wrapping paper.

Day 23

Spend the Day Dreaming about
A Far Away Place and then Draw this Picture

Day 24
Basic Fudge

Ingredients:
Margarine
2 cups sugar
3/4 cup milk
2 squares (2 ounces) unsweetened chocolate
1 tablespoon light corn syrup
dash of salt
1 teaspoon vanilla
2 tablespoons margarine

Directions: Lightly grease the bottom and sides of an 8x8x2-inch pan with margarine, or if thicker fudge is desired, use a 9x5x3-inch pan. Butter the sides of a heavy-gauge 2-quart saucepan. Clip a candy thermometer to side of pan. In the saucepan, stir together the sugar, milk, chocolate, corn syrup, and salt. Cook and stir over medium heat till sugar is dissolved and mixture begins to boil. Stir gently to avoid splashing syrup on sides of pan, which causes candy to become grainy. The mixture will begin to bubble vigorously and will rise close to pan rim. Use medium rather than high heat to prevent the mixture from sticking or boiling over.

Continue cooking the mixture, stirring only as necessary to prevent sticking, to 234° or the softball stage (a few drops of the mixture, dropped from a teaspoon into cold water, form a soft ball that flattens when removed from the water). Watch closely; temperature rises quickly above 220°.

Immediately remove pan from heat; add the 2 tablespoons margarine but do not stir. Cool mixture, without stirring or moving pan, until the thermometer registers 110°, or until the bottom of pan feels comfortably warm to the touch. Stirring or moving the mixture can result in grainy candy.

Remove the thermometer. Stir in vanilla; beat mixture by hand with a wooden spoon, lifting candy with an up-and-over motion, until the mixture becomes thick, starts to lose its gloss, and doesn't stream back into the pan when the spoon is lifted (or, till the mixture holds its shape when dropped onto waxed paper). Do not use an electric mixer.

Immediately spread fudge in the buttered pan. Cool; cut into squares. Store in a tightly covered container in a cool place. Makes about 40 pieces.

Day 25
Heart Hot Mitts

Materials: (for 2 mitts)
1/4 yard each of thick red and blue fabric;
1/2 yard calico (lining, appliqués);
quilt batting; red and blue bias tape.

Directions: Draw around your hand to make a mitten-shaped pattern. Cut two red, two blue, four calico, and four batting pieces using the mitten pattern. Applique four thumb and finger guards and four hearts cut from calico to mitts. Sandwich batting between lining and mitts. With wrong sides facing, sew front and backs together, leaving bottom open. Sew bias tape to outside edges.

Day 26
Apricot-Cashew Drops

Ingredients:

1 egg	1/4 cup packed brown sugar
1 teaspoon vanilla	1/2 cup granulated sugar
1/4 cup margarine	1/4 cup shortening
1 1/4 cups all-purpose flour	3/4 teaspoon salt
1/2 teaspoon baking soda	1/2 cup snipped dried apricots
1/2 cup chopped cashews	

Directions: In a mixer bowl cream together sugars, margarine, shortening, egg, vanilla, apricots, and cashews. Stir together flour, salt, and baking soda; stir into creamed mixture. Blend well. Drop from a teaspoon 2 inches apart onto a greased cookie sheet. Bake in a 375° oven for 8 to 10 minutes. Let stand 30 seconds. Remove from cookie sheet to a wire rack. Cool. Makes 3 dozen cookies.

Day 27

Magical Costume Trunk

Gather your friends together and spend a couple of days making costumes for your costume trunk (just like Lucy in *Lucy and the Beauty Queen*).

Materials:
Large cedar box or large cardboard box or large plastic storage box
Paint
Paint markers

Directions: Paint the box a rich color like purple or dark blue. Wait until the paint is dry, then use the paint markers to draw swirls, stars, moons, or other objects on the box.

Day 28

Costume-making Party

Gather your friends together and spend a couple of days making costumes for your costume trunk (just like Lucy in *Lucy and the Beauty Queen*).

Materials: Capes, vests, old adult-size clothing, couple of long pieces of any fabric, old sheet or curtain, lace or other sheer see-through fabric.

Old gloves, belts, hats, purses, costume jewelry, fake flowers and feathers, fur boa.
Crepe, tissue and construction paper to make feathers, flowers, or hats.
Wooden and glass beads, dried pumpkin seeds, tubular macaroni, and leather thronging, strings and synthetic raffia.
Pipe cleaners to make antennas, spectacles, headbands, jewelry.
Floral wire and other flexible wire to make jewelry, spectacles, halos, and to secure flowers and feathers in place.
Poster board, aluminium paper, aluminium baking pans, poster paints, markers, vinyl etc. to create crazy hats, ponchos, etc.
Small, light lampshades can be converted into hats.
Egg cartons, styrofoam trays, clear plastic trays from cookie bags, to make hel-

mets.

Pom-pons, tassles, ribbons, lace, buttons, corks, bottle caps, egg shaped panty-hose containers.

Frames from old sunglasses to use as spectacles. Decorate the frames with aluminum paper, paper rays, yarn, glitter etc. if desired.

Scraps of longhaired fur, or craft fur, to make mustaches, bushy eyebrows, beards.

Onion bags

Shower caps

Small and large scarves to wrap around head or neck or to tie around waist as sash, or around shoulders as shawl.

Old colanders and bowls

Old white sport socks

Solid Styrofoam cushioning from electronic appliances

Damaged and discarded Christmas garlands

Round large plastic bottles (such as chlorine bleach or fabric softener bottles) that are washed well and dried.

Leftover ribbons, cord, and yarn

Leftover wallpaper and gift paper, brown wrapping paper, brown grocery bags

Old rubber ball

Large cone-shaped popcorn containers

Inflatable broken children's pool

Old clothing

Scraps of felt and other fabrics

Old shower curtains

Costumes to Make

Gift Box Costume
Directions: With a square, lightweight box, remove the top and turn the box upside down. Glue pretty paper or comic pages on each side and top. Cut holes for the wearer's head and arms. Wrap wide ribbon around the box and glue or staple it in place. Then tie a huge bow on the wearer's head.

Old-Fashioned Nurse Costume
Directions: Create an old-fashioned nurse headdress first by cutting a large semicircle from white fabric or crepe paper to go around the head and tie at the back. Use a man's white shirt as the dress. Shorten sleeves by rolling it up. If you can sew, then baste the sleeves. Tie a belt around the waist. Cut red crosses from fabric or felt and glue them to the front of the pocket, headdress and bag.

Chef Costume

Directions: Cut a strip of white poster board about 3 x 22" long and glue or sew it into a circle. Pleat a large circle about 26" in diameter of white, stiff fabric or crepe paper all around edges, and sew or staple it under band. Hold up the hat with a crumble paper bag under the crown. Wear a white pair of pants and a white shirt. Then tie a white scarf around your neck.

Cowboy or Cowgirl Costume

Directions: Attach a cord chinstrap to an old hat or make one from a paper bag and cardboard – put a paper bag upside down on your head, shorten to desired length and glue a large overall made from brown cardboard for the brim. An overall hole should be cut in the middle of the cardboard oval that is slightly smaller than your head. Wear a plaid shirt. Tie a scarf around the neck. Cut a vest from brown felt. Wear jeans and boots.

Day 29

Costume-making Party

This is continued from the day before.

Doctor Costume

Directions: Create a Headlight for your head by cutting a circle out of an aluminum pie plate, paint on yellow rays with poster paint or acrylic paint or glue a sparkling button in the middle for a light. Attach this to an elastic band to fit on your head. Make a stethoscope by tying a cord around your neck with ends knotted inside a funnel. Wear an oversized white shirt with a shirt pocket. Cut from cardboard a thermometer and tongue depressor to fit in your pocket.

Hawaiian Hula Dancer Costume

Directions: Wear a skin tone leotard and tights. Add a hula skirt made from green crepe paper cut into the length of a skirt to wrap around your waist. Shred the green crepe paper into grass-like texture. Then put on a flower lei necklace from yellow, pink, blue and purple crepe paper flowers. If you have a long black wig, wear the wig with a big flower tuck behind your ear.

Magician Costume

Directions: Make a top hat from black poster board. Tie a red ribbon around the hat. Cut a black mustache from felt and stick it under your nose with rolled-up plastic bandage. Wear a black cape with red lining. Wear black pants with a wide red sash tied around the waist. Carry a black stick for a wand.

Butterfly Costume
Directions: Attach 2 long pipe cleaners on a headband for antennas. Take two sheets of poster board and draw a butterfly large enough to cover your chest and hips. Paint a butterfly pattern on the poster boards and cut. Punch holes at the waist and shoulders of both sets of the poster boards and tie them together with ribbons.

Day 30

Fingerprints

Can be played with a group of 2 to 10 people.

Materials:
Ink pad
index cards

Directions: Using an inkpad, have everyone make a print of their index finger on an index card. Write their names on the back of the card. Then collect all the cards. See if anyone can guess whose fingerprints belong to whom.

Day 31

Shadow Puppet Show

Can be played with a group of 2 to 10 people.

Materials: Post board (about 9" x 12") per puppet
scissors, X-acto knife, hole puncher, 4 paper fasteners per puppet,
2 wire coat hangers per puppet,
wire cutters, pliers, tape

Directions: Sketch the outline of your figure (a girl or a boy) on the poster board that is large enough so that the shoulder and elbow joints are at least 1/2" wide. Keep the shoulder to elbow joints separate from the elbow to finger joints and from the body.
Cut the figure out with a pair of scissors. Use the X-acto knife to cut out any interior sections like eyes or ears.

Punch holes in the shoulders and in the shoulder and elbow joints of the two arms.

Fasten all parts together (the finger to elbow joint to the elbow to shoulder joint and then this to the shoulder of the body) with fasteners. Fasten loose enough so that the joints bend easily. Cut off the paper fasteners with the wire cutters so they don't show when the arms are moved about.

Cut a wire coat hanger (snip off the bent hook completely) the length of the puppet plus about 8". Bend it with the pliers so that it conforms to the figure. Tape the wire in place with short lengths of tape. Cut 2 wires for the arms from the other coat hanger (about 18" long or long enough so that you can raise the puppet's arms high, but still have your hands hidden). Wrap some tape around one end of each wire several times; then tape the wires to the puppet's hands. Use the puppet behind a lit screen.

Day 32

Ham and Cheese Roll-Ups

Ingredients:
4 ounces deli-thin low-moisture part-skim mozzarella cheese slices (or similar)
12 slices 97% fat-free deli-thin honey or smoked ham slices

Directions: Using a plastic knife, with a help of an adult, cut the cheese slices into strips of 3 equal pieces. Place one strip on top of the ham slice. Roll up the ham and cheese together, starting from the bottom and rolling toward the top to make a log shape. Repeat with the other 11 slices of ham and cheese. Spear with a colorful toothpick or fancy cocktail plastic toothpick if desired. Otherwise, place each roll-up in a Ziploc bag until needed or wrap each lunch serving in foil or a sandwich bag. This makes 12 roll-ups.

Day 33

Spinmaster

The President and other public figures have a team of writers and spokespersons to make events that would seem negative seem more positive. Imagine you are this team of writers and spokespersons.

Materials: Pins, pencils, paper

Directions: Pick each person from your group (if you have a small group) or a couple of persons from your group (if the group is large), and write down a list of things you know about this person. Write both positive and negatives adjectives. If you have any negative words, point out positive alternatives for those words. For example: fearful (cautious), talkative (sociable) and more.

Day 34

Memento Line

Materials:
Clothesline
Clothespins
Birthday cards
Pictures
Postcards

Directions: String a clothesline along one of your walls or you can string it from one wall to another. Pin special pictures, postcards or your birthday cards on the clothespins. This will keep them in mind of things you love!

Day 35

Peanut Butter Marble Fudge

Ingredients:
Margarine
2 cups sugar
3/4 cup milk
2 squares (2 ounces) unsweetened chocolate
1 tablespoon light corn syrup
dash of salt
1 teaspoon vanilla
2 tablespoons margarine
3/4 cup peanut butter

Directions: Lightly grease the bottom and sides of an 8x8x2-inch pan with margarine, or if thicker fudge is desired, use a 9x5x3-inch pan. Butter the sides of a heavy-gauge 2-quart saucepan. Clip a candy thermometer to side of pan. In the saucepan, stir together the sugar, milk, chocolate, corn syrup, and salt. Cook and stir over medium heat till sugar is dissolved and mixture begins to boil. Stir gently to avoid splashing syrup on sides of pan, which causes candy to become grainy. The mixture will begin to bubble vigorously and will rise close to pan rim. Use medium rather than high heat to prevent the mixture from sticking or boiling over.

Continue cooking the mixture, stirring only as necessary to prevent sticking, to 234° or the softball stage (a few drops of the mixture, dropped from a teaspoon into cold water, form a soft ball that flattens when removed from the water). Watch closely; temperature rises quickly above 220°.

Immediately remove pan from heat; add the 2 tablespoons margarine but do not stir. Cool mixture, without stirring or moving pan, till thermometer registers 110°, or till bottom of pan feels comfortably warm to the touch. Stirring or moving the mixture can result in grainy candy.

Remove the thermometer. Stir in vanilla; beat mixture by hand with a wooden spoon, lifting candy with an up-and-over motion, till mixture becomes thick, starts to lose its gloss, and doesn't stream back into the pan when the spoon is lifted (or, till the mixture holds its shape when dropped onto waxed paper). Stir in peanut butter; swirl once or twice to marble. Do not use an electric mixer.

Immediately spread fudge in the buttered pan. Cool; cut into squares. Store in a tightly covered container in a cool place. Makes about 40 pieces.

Day 36
Bird Topiary

Materials:
14 or 15-gauge wire about 52" long
Wire cutters
Pliers
Twist ties
Waterproof tape
Small stones or gravel
Ivy plant, growing in a 4" pot

Directions:
Cut a piece of wire about 42" long. Bend it into the bird shape shown or into your own shape. The base of this bird takes about 8" of wire, the central "stem" another 8", and the bird itself the remaining wire. Fasten the end of the wire to the central stem with a twist tie.

For a fuller, more three-dimensional shape, add a 10" circle of wire to the midsection. Attach it with twist ties. Cover the entire frame with waterproof tape.

Remove the ivy plant from the pot by holding it upside-down and giving it a shake. The plant should drop out, soil and all.

Place the frame in the pot. Anchor it with some small rocks; then replace the ivy plant and its soil. Start training the plant right away by wrapping a long piece of ivy around the central stem and up to the bird shape.

Keep the plant in a bright spot, but away from direct sunlight (you can keep it in a windowsill but make sure it's facing north or east). Turn the plant now and again so that it grows evenly on all sides. Trim the plant as it grows. Wherever you cut a stem, it will branch off into two stems, which is the trick to getting the ivy to completely cover the frame. Water the plant when the soil feels dry, but don't over water it. Give the ivy a dose of fertilizer every month, and it should live a long happy life.

Day 37

Learn American Sign Language (ASL)

Day 38

Flower Bulbs Gift

Materials:
3 terra-cotta flowerpots, about 4 1/2" in diameter
Orange, yellow, light green, and white acrylic paints
3 pieces yellow cotton fabric, 14 x 20 inches each
4 to 6 bulbs each of 3 different flowers
Ribbon in orange, yellow, and green; 24 inches each
3 wooden skewers
1 narrow and 1 wide paintbrush
Plastic container
Sponge
Paper towel
Scissors
Glass
Pencil
Tape

Directions: Paint pots yellow, orange, and green with the narrow brush. Dilute white paint with water. Moisten sponge and dip into diluted paint. Squeeze out excess paint, and pat sponge over each pot's surface. Let dry. Dip bristle tips of wide brush in undiluted paint. Dab excess onto paper towel, then brush over surface. Repeat. Let dry. At 1 long edge of fabric, turn 4" to wrong side. Overlap short edges 2 inches, gather bottom, and tie to form bags. Place bags in pots and fill each with 1 type of bulb. Tie bag shut with ribbon that matches the paint on the pot. Using a glass cup as a template, draw a circle around the picture of each type of flower on bulb package and cut out. Tape pictures onto the skewers. Insert into pot to identify its contents.

Day 39
Read a good Biography

Day 40
Special Guests Gala

In this game, everyone in the group gets to be their favorite celebrity, historical figure, or fictional figure at a gathering. Without telling anyone who they are, each person will take their turn telling one thing about their famous person. Then the rest of the group has to guess who that celebrity is. Groups of 3 and more persons.

Day 41
Decorated Mason Jars

Groups of 2 or more people can work on this.

Materials: Mason jars
colorful ribbons
colorful fabric
zigzag scissors
glitter glue, glue, paint, stickers

Directions: There are many ways you can decorate a mason jar. Be creative! Here are a few ideas to get you started:

Decorate the jar and lid with colorful stickers.
Using the glitter glue and paint, write your name or draw a picture.
Glue scraps of fabric onto the jar.

Cut a big circle (about 12 inches wide) out of a colorful fabric with zigzag scissors and wrap it over the lid of the jar and tie a ribbon around the neck of the jar to hold it decoratively in place.

Tie a colorful ribbon around the neck of the jar. You can tie the ribbon through a set of measuring spoons for a little added gift and decoration.

Day 42

Room Refresh Spray!

Materials: 4 ounces fresh or 2 ounces dried chemical-free fragrant flowers like jasmine, carnation, lemon geranium, rose, lavender or lilac
3 cloves
1 1/2 cups distilled water
1 drop lemon essential oil
8-ounce glass spray bottle with tight-fitting lid
Scissors
Tall glass jar with tight-fitting lid
Fine sieve
2 glass pitchers
Paper coffee filter
Small funnel

Directions: Remove any insects from flowers. Cut flower heads off stems. Put flowers and cloves in tall sterilized jar. Heat distilled water until warm but not boiling. Pour enough water into jar to cover flowers completely. Secure lid; shake well. Place in warm, sunny spot where it can remain undisturbed. Let flowers steep in distilled water, shaking jar occasionally, for about 2 weeks. Pour contents through sieve into sterilized pitcher, then through coffee filter over second pitcher. Add 1 drop lemon essential oil; mix. Using small funnel, transfer liquid to sterilized spray bottle. Spray to freshen room or linens.

Day 43
Treasured Art Apron

Groups of 2 or more people can work on this.

Materials:
Apron
Your artwork or a picture of yourself or picture of gift recipient
Iron/ironing board
Iron-on transfer paper
Photocopier

Directions: Photocopy desired artwork onto iron-on transfer paper. Place transfer on apron as desired. Iron on artwork, following manufacturer's instructions.

Day 44
Try a Hot Chocolate Party Instead of a Tea Party.

Day 45
Plant Pincushions

Materials:
Green and red print fabrics
fiberfill
pipe cleaners;
clay pots;
pebbles.

Directions: Cut two flower shapes. Sew pieces together with right sides facing. Leave an opening. Turn, stuff, and sew opening.

Cut and piece two leaves. Attach leaves to pipe-cleaner stem; sew stem to flower and cut stem to desired length. Cut cactus pieces from green print fabric. Stitch and stuff individual pieces; attach small pieces to cactus form. Place "plants" in clay pots; secure with decorative pebbles or small stones.

Day 46
Colonial Pomander Ball

Materials:
Large apple
Box of cloves (from a supermarket)
Cinnamon
Plastic net bag or 8" square of nylon net (fabric stores will have this)
Cord, ribbon, or yarn

Directions: Prick the skin of the apple with a fork. Into each hole insert eh stem of a whole clove. Keep pricking and inserting cloves until the whole apple is completely covered. Place the apple in a shallow bowl and sprinkle with cinnamon. Set in a cool, dry spot for a few days. Then shake off any excess cinnamon. To hang the ball, cut ends off a net bag-making piece about 10" long. Slip the apple inside. Gather ends at bottom; tie a bow with cord or bright-colored yarn. Tie knot forming a 6" loop. Gather net over top of ball, wind ends of cord around and tie another knot. Tie a yarn bow over the knot and hang.

Day 47
Drawing in the Dark

Can be played with 2 or more Players

A player is chosen as a storyteller. The rest of the players are given a paper and a pencil, crayon, or marker. Then the lights are turned out. The storyteller then proceeds to tell a story that is short and simple that the players must illustrate. The story should include different people, animals and objects that the storyteller instructs the players to draw. The players are given a minute or so to draw the people or animals in the story, before the story continues with the storyteller pausing for a few moments after each new element is added to the tale. When everyone has finished drawing the lights are turned on. Then everyone gets to see what was drawn.

Day 48
Visit a Pick-Your-Own Farm

Day 49
Funky Fun Summer Sandals

Materials:
Clear cement glue
Decorative elements like beads, rhinestones, silk flowers, sequins, and shells
Nylon thread
Thong

Directions: Glue decorative elements onto thongs. Attach beaded strands to thongs straps with thread. Knot to secure.

Day 50
Mini Character Pancakes

Ingredients:
Cookie cutters
Pancake Mix

Directions: Follow directions on the pancake mix package, but pour pancake batter into cookie cutters to create small character pancakes.

Day 51
Go Ice Skating

Directions: Grab some friends and go ice skating (either indoors or outdoors.)

Day 52
Hero's Welcome

Material:
Any object like a cool hat, a bracelet, or a scarf.

Directions: Take turns at being a hero. Give the person chosen as a hero the object while you announce how this incredible person single-handedly achieved something wonderful like –

Solved world hunger
Discover a cure for the common cold
Ended all wars

Or some possible real accomplishments like:

Washed the dishes without being told
Helped a friend with their chores
Turn in a homework assignment
Practice piano
Feed the pet bird
Babysat her little brother
Helped Mom prepare dinner
Took out the trash
Read a story to an elderly friend

Everyone in the group one by one walks up to the hero and gives a hug and a kiss or words of praise or gratefulness or a pat on the back.

Day 53

Garden in a Box

Materials:
Glass aquarium, at least 10-gallon size
Gravel
Charcoal
Potting soil
Humidity-loving plants (African violets, ferns or mosses)
Mister

Directions: Wash the aquarium with soap and water; rinse well. Place a 1/2" layer of gravel on the bottom of the aquarium. On top of this sprinkle a layer of charcoal. Put about 2" of damp potting soil over this. Remove each plant from its pot by holding it upside-down in one hand and giving the pot a sharp tap. The plant should fall right out into your hand. Make a shallow depression for each plant in the potting soil. Place each plant in position, spreading its roots out horizontally and packing potting soil around it. (This will slow the growth of the plants.) Arrange the plants so that there is a focal point (a colorful plant or a taller plant) and an interesting mix of colors and textures as if you were planning a drawing. Spray the plants with the mister. Cover the top of the aquarium with a sheet of glass or with foil. Place the terrarium in indirect light, away from a heater.

Day 54
Colorful Screen

Materials:
Colorful Plastic drinking straws
String or strong thread
Needle
A wood dowel or bamboo pole wider than the screen you want to make
Colorful wooden beads
2 Screw hooks
1 red acrylic paint
Brush

Directions: Measure out a long piece of strong thread. Thread the needle: then pass it through a wooden bead. Tie the bead in place with a secure knot. Cut the straws into different lengths, and pass the needle through two longer ones. Make a bundle of six or seven short lengths, lay them horizontally, and pierce them with the needle. Continue the pattern, leaving enough thread to attach the line to the pole. When finished, hang the screen on the hooks.

Day 55
Stuffed Pancakes from Lebanon

Ingredients:
Filling:
2 cups chopped walnuts
2 teaspoons cinnamon
3 tablespoons sugar

Syrup:
1 cup pancake syrup or dark corn syrup

Batter:

1 envelope active dry yeast   11/2 cups all-purpose flour
1 teaspoon sugar   1/2 cup vegetable oil
1 1/4 to 2 cups lukewarm water

Directions: Dissolve yeast and sugar in 1/2 cup warm water. Cover lightly with a damp cloth and leave in a warm place for about 20 minutes or until mixture begins to foam.

In a small bowl, mix walnuts, sugar, and cinnamon. Set aside. Warm a large mixing bowl by rinsing with hot water and drying thoroughly. Sift flour into warmed bowl. Make a depression in the center, pour in yeast mixture, and beat into the flour. Continue beating, gradually adding water until mixture is the consistency of pancake batter.

Cover mixture with a damp cloth and leave in a warm place for 1 hour or until bubbly.

Heat a heavy skillet over high heat. When hot, add 1-teaspoon oil and swirl to coat skillet evenly. Pour 1/4 cup batter into pan. Tilt pan gently to even out batter, but keep pancake fairly thick and round. Cook until it begins to bubble and comes away easily from pan. Cook only one side of pancake. Repeat with remaining batter, adding oil to pan as needed.

Put 2 tablespoons filling on uncooked side of each pancake and fold in half. Pinch edges together firmly to keep filling in place. Pour 2 tablespoons oil into skillet and fry folded pancakes about 2 to 3 minutes on each side or until golden brown. Drain well on paper towels. Dip pancakes in syrup while they are still warm and serve with sour cream or cottage cheese.

Day 56

Learn to Type

Day 57

Game of Sardines

Can be played with 6 or more Players

In this game full of wiggles and giggles, the biggest challenge is to keep from giving the hiding place away by laughing. Instead of one "it" searching for all the other players, each player seeks to join the others in one hiding spot. Sardines are most fun when played in an area with lots of safe places to hide.

To begin, all players except one close their eyes. The open-eyed player hides while the others count to 100. The hiding space should be just roomy enough for several people, but not too big. Good choices are behind a curtain, behind a leafy bush or under a slide. When the counting is finished, a second player searches for the first while the others keep their eyes closed and count to 100 again. If the first player is found, the second joins him in the hiding place. If not, the seeker is out of the game. Play continues in this manner until each child has had a chance to be the seeker.

The game is over when all the players have had their turn to seek. All the sardines packed in the hiding spot are winners.

Day 58

Flower and Plant Press

Materials:
2 pieces of 1/4" inch plywood or masonite cut to size to a 6" x 8" rectangle each.

Directions: Drill 1" inch holes in the four corners of each board and attach them to one another with long bolts topped with wing nuts. Cut several pieces of cardboard the size of your press. Trim a triangle off each corner where the bolts go. Tighten the nuts evenly at all four corners to put enough pressure on the plants to press them.

Day 59

Pressed Flower Bookmark

Materials:
Flower blossoms, leaves, ferns, and grasses
Clean scrap paper
Fat book or plant press
Heavy paper, about 2 1/2 ” x 2 1/2” x 8”
Clear Contact ® paper, enough to cover paper
X-acto knife

Directions: 1 or 2 weeks before, pick blossoms and leaves that are fresh and dry to be press between the pages of a thick book or between the layers of cardboard in your press. Press the plants for 1-2 weeks or until they are completely dry. Lay all the pressed plant material out so that you can see what you have to work with. Handle the plants carefully as they are fragile. Try to plan an arrangement in your head or sketch it out on paper first to avoid moving the plants around too much. Glue the pressed flowers and leaves to the piece of heavy paper. Glue sparingly. Cover the entire bookmark with a piece of clear Contact ® paper that is slightly larger than the bookmark. Lay it over the plants, starting at on end. Rub your fingers over the Contact ® paper as you lower it to press out any air bubbles. Trim the excess Contact ® paper from the perimeter of the bookmark.

Day 60

Muslim Letter Sorter

Materials:
2 1/2 yards unbleached muslim; rubber stamps and pads.

Directions: Pre-shrink muslin; press. Cut three 131/2x201/2-inch muslin rectangles. Layer these, making sure edges are even. This forms the backing for the pockets. Cut eight 131/2x13-inch rectangles for pockets. Fold each in half so pockets are 131/2 inches wide and 61/2 inches deep; press. Position one pocket, folded edge up, on backing so that folded edge is 2 inches below the top. Pin sides and bottom of pocket.

Stitch sides and bottom of pocket to backing, using 5/8-inch seam allowances. Position next pocket, folded edge up, 1 3/4 inches down from folded edge of pocket already in place; stitch. Repeat with six remaining pockets. Trim the overhanging pocket so that it is flush with bottom edge of backing.

Round all corners. Cut two 51/2x23/4-inch strips; fold in half, then stitch to top of sorter for hanging loops. Sew 3-inch-wide, bias-cut muslin pieces together for edging. Beginning at center bottom, pin strips to sorter, folding raw edges under and easing strips around corners.

Practice stamping letters on scrap muslin. Use a variety of stamp pad colors, and strive for a loose, casual placement of the letters. Once you master lettering, apply labels to pockets.

Day 61
Go Bowling

Day 62
Create a Secret Sanctuary

Directions: -Find a place in your house or your backyard that you can go to when you want a quiet place to think. Then decorate it with comfortable and peaceful things like pillows, candles, and photos.

Day 63
Oatmeal-Chocolate Chippers

Ingredients:

1 egg   1/4 cup packed brown sugar
1 teaspoon vanilla   1/2 cup granulated sugar
1/4 cup margarine   1/4 cup shortening
1 cup all-purpose flour   3/4 teaspoon salt
1/2 teaspoon baking soda   1 cup semisweet chocolate pieces
1 cup quick-cooking rolled oats 1/2 cup chopped walnuts
2 tablespoon milk

Directions: In a mixer bowl cream together sugars, margarine, shortening, egg, vanilla, and milk. Stir together flour, salt, chocolate, oats, walnuts, and baking soda; stir into creamed mixture. Blend well. Drop from a teaspoon 2 inches apart onto a greased cookie sheet. Bake in a 375° oven for 8 to 10 minutes. Let stand 30 seconds. Remove from cookie sheet to a wire rack. Cool. Sprinkle with remaining chopped toasted almonds. Makes 31/2 dozen cookies.

Day 64

Marble Desk Accessories

Materials:
Medium-weight paper
Oil paints in 2 or 3 colors
Turpentine or mineral spirits
Paper cups
Plastic dishpan or deep tray
Paintbrush
Small stick
Notebook
Rubber cement

Directions: Thin each oil paint color with a little turpentine in the paper cups so that the paint is thin enough to shake easily from a brush, but not too runny. Fill the dishpan with room temperature water (65-70°F) at least 3" deep. With the paintbrush, sprinkle small drops of each color onto the water. Use a small stick, such as a toothpick, to make swirling designs in the water. Don't over mix or the colors will get muddy. Hold the paper by opposite corners and carefully lower it onto the water. Let it lie flat, and then lift it out of the water. Dry the paper flat, design-side up, on newspaper o hang to dry. Glue the paper to the cover of a notebook such as a spiral-bound pad. Trim any excess off.

Day 65

Go Fishing with your grandfather or someone older.

Day 66

Go roller skating or roller blading

Day 67

Juicicles!

Ingredients:
3 types of fruit juice (lemonade, orange, apple, raspberry)

Directions: Wash the plastic Popsicle molds and Popsicle sticks. After the Popsicle molds are clean and dry, fill them with the juices you have selected. Once the molds are filled, add the sticks and then place the Popsicles in your freezer. One or two hours later, depending on the size of the mold, your Popsicles will be ready!

Day 68

Take a Positive Stance – Do the Positive Dance!

Directions: You can do this alone or with a group of friends. Do this whenever you need a pick-me-up! Slump over with your head, shoulders, arms dragging to the ground and say, "I can't. I can't. It's too hard. It's not fair. I'm too small. I'm too weak. I can't." Then stand up, reaching as high as possible with your hands to touch the sky. Say out loud, " I CAN! Yes, I CAN! I can do it! I am smart. I can learn. I do know. Yes I CAN!" Repeat this until you feel you truly can. At the end, give yourself a hand and a cheer!

Day 69

Prepare Hiking or Camping Food for a Day Hike

Chicken-Noodle Soup Mix Packet for Hiking or Gift

Ingredients:
1/2 cup dried chicken cubes
1/2 cup dried noodles
1/4 cup chopped dried carrots

1/4 cup chopped dried celery
1/4 cup dried green peas
1 tablespoon chopped dried onion
2 tablespoons chicken bouillon powder or cubes

Directions: Combine all ingredients and mix well. Seal in a plastic freezer bag. To serve, simmer over a campfire or camp stove in 2 quarts boiling water until vegetables and meat are tender, about 1 hour. Stir occasionally and add water as necessary. Season to taste with salt and pepper.

Campfire Beans and Ham

Ingredients:
1 1/2 cups dried beans – Great Northern, navy, pinto, and kidney
1/2 cup dried ham, chopped
1/4 cup dried onion, chopped
1/4 cup dried carrot, grated
2 tablespoons dried green pepper
1 tablespoon chicken broth powder or 3 chicken bouillon cubes
1 teaspoon salt
1/8 teaspoon pepper

Directions: Mix all ingredients well. Store in a plastic freezer bag. To serve, add to 3 quarts water in a stewing kettle. Simmer over hot coals or medium heat on a camp stove 2 to 3 hours, until beans are tender, stirring occasionally and adding water if necessary.

Banana Chip Pudding

Ingredients:
1 package vanilla flavored instant pudding
1/2 cup dried banana chips
1/2 cup dried milk powder

Directions: Mix ingredients well. Store in a plastic freezer bag. To serve, stir in water according to directions on pudding package. Beat with a fork. Divide into 4 dishes. Let set 10 minutes.

Whole Grain Cornbread

Ingredients:
1 1/2 cups whole grain mix
3/4 cup ground dried corn
1 tablespoon powdered dried egg (or 1 egg)
1/2 cup water

Directions: Combine all ingredients. Stir just until blended. Pour into a well-greased 8-inch square baking pan or a pan made by folding a doubled thickness of heavy duty aluminum foil into a pan shape, then greasing well. Bake in a camp stove oven or over medium heat or in a Dutch oven or reflector oven over hot coals. Bake until a straw inserted in the middle comes out clean. Baking time depends on the temperature of the fire.

Hot Tomato Broth

Ingredients:
Place 3 tablespoons powdered tomato puree in a cup. Fill cup with boiling water and stir well. Season to taste with salt. Serve hot or cold.

Day 70
Day Hike

Can be with a group of 2 and more.
Make sure an adult accompanies the group.

Directions: With a group of 2 or more people, armed with snacks and hiking or camping food, go hiking for a day. Bring water and a good map of the area you are hiking. Wear good hiking shoes. If you intend to stay overnight, bring along extra clothing and camping gear for the night.

Day 71

Overnight Camping (Backyard Version)

You can camp out in your own backyard!

Materials:
A tent for 2 or more persons. If you do not have a tent, then a waterproof canvas, large enough to drape over a pole or tree branch to create a tent. 2 poles. 4 wooden stakes and rubber hammer. Sleeping bags, lantern, flashlight, bug spray (if needed).

Directions: Invite one or two friends over for a camp-out in your backyard. Set up your ready-made tent or drape your canvas over a tree branch. If you don't have a tree nearby, set one pole into the ground and the other pole about 5 or 6 feet away. Drape the canvas over the 2 poles so it forms a tent. At each corner of the tent, stake down the corner into the ground with the rubber hammer. If you have extra canvas, cover the inside of the tent with it for ground covering. Then unfold your sleeping bags, turn on the lantern. Take turns telling scary stories and pointing out stars in the sky.

Day 72

Smell A Memory

Materials:
Cotton swabs.
Perfume, detergent, herbs, candy, popcorn, fruit or anything that is a constant scent in your family.

Directions: Swab the cotton swabs with each of the fragrances. Then have a family member close his eyes, smell deeply and describe a kind of memory associated with that smell. Then switch.

Day 73

Puppet Show

Put together a puppet show with your friends for all your families.

Note from Emily Cobbs:
You're Doing Great!

Make Every Day Count!

Day 74

Ghost in the Graveyard

Can be played with 3 or more Players

In this game, one player is chosen as the "ghost" who hides while the others count. Choose a nice big area to set up the game, preferably where there is a tree, porch, or other large, stationary object to serve as home base. Since this is played in the dark, make sure the space is clear of any tree roots, sprinklers or anything else that people can trip over.

Choose one player as the ghost. Then the other players close their eyes and count to 50 or up to 100 at the home base while the ghost hides. Then the players set out to hunt for the ghost, while the ghost tries to take them by surprise and to tag as many players as possible before they make it back to home base. Set aside a rule that no one is allowed to stay within a certain distance to the base to make it fair for everyone so no one stays too close to home base. Any player who spots the ghost yells to the other players to warn them to dash to the home base. Those tagged by the ghost are out until the end of the round, which is when all the players are either tagged or have reached home safely. At the end of each round, the players who have reached the base safely close their eyes and count to 50 or 100 again. Those who were tagged in previous rounds become ghosts and team up with the original ghost to chase down the remaining players. The last player to remain "alive" is the winner.

Day 75

Attend a Poetry Reading with Your Parent

Day 76
Lip Balm

Materials:
1 teaspoon beeswax
1 teaspoon cocoa butter
2 teaspoons sweet almond oil
2 drops rose oil
Shallow, wide mouthed tins or jars with lid
Large, shallow pan
Small stainless-steel pot
Whisk
Eyedropper

Directions: Bring water to a boil in pan or in bottom of double boiler. In small pot, melt beeswax and cocoa butter together over low heat, whisking until they liquefy. Add sweet almond oil, whisking to blend completely with melted beeswax and cocoa butter. Remove pot from heat; let cool slightly. Add rose oil; whisk until well blended. Pour liquid into tins or jars while it is still warm. Let balm cool completely. Seal containers. Decorate the containers if you like. Store in cool place and use within 6 months.

Day 77
Flatware Caddies

Materials:
1/2 yard solid-color fabric;
1/2 yard calico fabric;
bias tape;
quilt batting.

Directions: Cut a 16-inch-square napkin from calico; hem. Trace lozenge shape onto brown paper; cut two shapes from solid-color fabric and two from calico. Place quilt batting between solid and calico shapes; quilt pieces together with three evenly spaced vertical rows of stitches. Repeat for the second piece. Baste quilted pieces together, leaving top edge open. Cover edges with bias tape or pieced fabric strips. Fold top edge down in front.

Day 78

Visit the Local Animal Shelter
and spend the day petting the pets.

Day 79

Biography

Materials: Journal or notebook

Directions: Write a "book" about you! Include drawings and pictures in your book. Here are some possible chapters:

Where I was born
How I look – for example: brown hair, green eyes.
Where I live
Who lives with me
Where I've been
My school
My family
Neighbors and relatives
My friends
My favorite places I go to in town
My favorite foods
My favorite hobbies
Pets
My favorite books

Day 80

Caramel Popcorn Balls

Ingredients:
10 cups popped plain popcorn (low-fat microwave popping corn can also be used)
20 caramels
1 cup miniature marshmallows
2 tablespoons water
1 teaspoon vanilla extract

1/8 teaspoon ground cinnamon
low-fat or diet margarine

Directions: Pop the popcorn if it isn't popped yet, and then pour into the largest bowl you can find. Set aside. Unwrap the 20 caramels. Measure the marsh-mallows and water into a 2 – 4-cup glass measure or bowl. Add caramels to the glass measure or bowl and microwave on HIGH for about 11/2 minute. Stir and microwave 1 more minute. Stir the mixture until the marshmallows are completely melted (about a minute). Add in the vanilla and cinnamon. Pour immediately over the popped corn and toss until well coated and cooled. Lightly grease your hands with the margarine. Pack about a cup of the caramel corn into your hands into a ball (like a snowball). Wrap the balls up with plas-tic wrap. Tie with a festive ribbon. Repeat with the remaining caramel corn and place the popcorn balls in the refrigerator until needed.

Day 81

Build a Tree House

Day 82

Bowling

Materials:
Acrylic Paint: Orange and Yellow
Marbles or small pebbles
Craft glue
Paintbrushes
6 Rubber bands
6 Empty and Dry 2-liter Soda bottles
Large rubber ball
8" Fabric Square

Directions: Paint 3 bottles with orange paint, and 3 bottles in yellow paint. Drop about 12 marbles or pebbles into each container. Replace lids. Center square of fabric over top of container and secure on neck with rubber band. Start bowling by knocking down the pinks with the rubber ball.

Day 83

Take a walk to the park with an older friend
and feed the ducks or birds.

Day 84

Have a Pizza-Making Party

Ingredients:
French Bread
Mozzarella Cheese
Pizza Toppings – The usual or something new to experiment with: Pepperoni,
Sausages, chicken, ham, hot dogs, mushrooms, tomatoes, peppers, anchovies,
pineapples, pears, peaches, onions
Pizza Sauce
Bar B Q Sauce

Directions: Invite your friends over for a pizza-making party. Put the pizza toppings into small bowls next to each other. Cut the French bread into 1 inch
slices and lay out. Then lay out the pizza sauce or Bar B Q Sauce next to each
other. Everyone gets to make their own pizza. First take a slice of the bread,
cover the top with pizza sauce or Bar B Q Sauce, then put on any or all of the
toppings and a layer of cheese to create their own pizza. Put on microwave-
proof dish and microwave until toppings are cooked and cheese is melted.
When done, name each pizza by the maker's name. For instance, Jill's Hawaiian
Surprise or Susan's Tomato-Sausage Pizza.

Day 85

Make a "Sayings" Rock Garden

Materials:
Large flat rocks or stones
Paint
Brush
Markers

Directions: Create a rock that says something. Paint each rock. Then with
markers, write a favorite saying on the rock. You can also draw other decora-

tions on the rocks. These make good paperweights, displays in a rock garden, or even gifts.

Day 86
Exercise to an Exercise Video

Day 87
Orchestra

Directions: Grab a group of friends. Have each one make one sound: whistling, clapping, knee slapping, floor tapping, clucking, mooing, laughing, and anything they can think of. Then choose someone to be a conductor, using a finger as a baton, to indicate who should be playing, and if they should be playing softly or loudly.

Day 88
Caramel Chews

Ingredients:
1 tablespoon vegetable oil
6 ounces unsweetened or bittersweet chocolate
1 cup heavy cream
1 1/4 cups granulated sugar
1 cup powdered sugar
Clear cellophane

Directions: Line bottom and sides of 9 x 9" ceramic baking dish with parchment; brush or spray with vegetable oil. Using handheld metal grater and working over clean, dry plate, finely grate chocolate. Heat cream, grated chocolate and granulated sugar over medium heat, stirring continuously, until mixture thickens. Sift powdered sugar over mixture; stir until blended. Pour mixture into prepared baking dish. Cover dish and refrigerate at least 2 hours. Using sharp knife dipped in cold water, cut caramel into 1-inch cubes. Cut rectangles from cellophane. Wrap each candy, twisting ends to secure. Store in refrigerator up to 1 week.

Day 89

Blow some bubbles with a bubble-making machine.

Day 90

Create a Victory Drawer

Materials:
a drawer in your desk or bureau.

Directions: Designate a drawer to be where you put in files, pictures, mementos, etc. that remind you of your past achievements, how much you're loved, what you're good at, and anything that makes you feel good about yourself. Whenever you're feeling down, open up your drawer and pull out a "victory reminder".

Day 91

Go to a Play

Day 92

Explore Your Town

Directions: Go walking around your town and learn about the history of the buildings and people of your town. Keep a notepad with you to jot down the places you've visited and people you've met. Now you've learned something more about your town.

Day 93

Be a Tour Guide for Your Town

Directions: When a relative or friend come and visit you from out of town, you can act as a tour guide for them. Just by exploring your town a little and keeping a notepad of interesting facts about your town (Day 92), you can share with your relative or friend the history and stories of your special town.

Day 94

Visit the nearest Chinatown or cultural center!

Day 95

Good Thoughts Game

One good thought usually leads to others. Do this whenever you are feeling down.

Materials: Watch

Directions: Choose something to admire – a pretty flower, the sweet taste of ice cream or chocolate, how soft your pillow is, and more. Take turns with a family member or friend in admiring the object out loud. Keep talking for 20 seconds. Then switch.

Day 96

Write a Message in a Bottle and set it Free.

Day 97

Peanut Butter Chip Cookies

Ingredients:
2 1/4 cups all-purpose flour
1/3 cup Cocoa
1 teaspoon baking soda
1/2 teaspoon salt
1 cup or 2 sticks softened butter or margarine
3/4 cup granulated sugar
3/4 cup packed light brown sugar
1 teaspoon vanilla extract
2 eggs
2 cups or 12-oz. Package Peanut Butter Chips
1 cup chopped nuts

Directions: Heat oven to 375° F. Stir together flour, cocoa, baking soda and salt. Beat butter, granulated sugar, brown sugar and vanilla in large bowl on medium speed of mixer until creamy. Add eggs; beat well. Gradually add flour mixture, beating well. Stir in peanut butter chips, beat well. Gradually add flour mixture, beating well. Stir in peanut butter chips. Add nuts, if desired. Drop by rounded teaspoons onto ungreased cookie sheet. Bake 8 to 10 minutes or until set. Cool slightly, remove from cookie sheet to wire rack. Makes about 5 dozen cookies.

Day 98

Flower Decoupage Plate

Materials:

Book-dried or pressed flowers, leaves or ferns
White paper or plastic plate
Crayons
Liquid white glue
Paper cup
Paintbrush
Tweezers
Plastic wrap or aluminum foil
Stick-on picture hanger

Directions: Make book-dried or pressed flowers, leaves or ferns first. (See Day 59.) Decorate the inside rim of the plate with a crayon design. Pour liquid white glue into a paper cup. Paint the bottom of the inside of the plate with a coating of the glue. Using the tweezers, carefully pick up the dried flowers and leaves from the paper. Arrange them on the glued surface. Paint over the flowers with a light coating of glue. Allow the glue to dry completely. While the plate is drying, cover the glue in the cup with plastic wrap or foil. Give the entire plate a second coating of glue after the first coating has dried. When dry, stick a picture hanger on the back of the plate to hang.

Day 99
Sparkly Locker Mirrors

Materials:
Extra-strength magnets
Glass glue
Round mirror about 4" diameter
Round rhinestones such as yellow, green, pink, blue

Directions: Glue three magnets onto back of each square mirror. Glue two magnets onto back of round mirror. Arrange and glue square rhinestones around edges of square mirrors, alternating colors as desired. Arrange and glue round rhinestones around edges of round mirror, alternating colors as desired. Let dry.

Day 100
Brighter Outlook

Directions: Take turns with a friend or family member in seeing the brighter side of life. Imagine positive outcomes to negative experiences.

For instance:
You don't get invited to a friend's party.
You end up going to the movies with your favorite aunt.

You didn't make the basketball team.
You get chosen by a visiting talent scout to be the star of a new movie.

Day 101
Sandwich Flutes

Ingredients:
1/2 ripe tomato, thinly sliced
2/3 cup shredded lettuce (optional)
1 to 2 tablespoons light garlic and herb spreadable cheese (or use light mayonnaise mixed with grated reduced-fat cheddar cheese)
2 soft flour tortillas (fajita or thick homestyle)

4 slices 97% fat-free deli-thin ham or turkey breast

Makes 2 sandwich flutes.

Directions: Thinly slice the tomato with a plastic knife if you are under 9 years old and shred the lettuce, if desired. Spread 1/2 to 1 tablespoon of the garlic and herb spreadable cheese evenly over one of the tortillas. Have your child lay two slices of the ham or turkey over the top of the tortilla toward the center. Then have your child place a few tomato slices down the center and about 1/3 cup of the shredded lettuce, if desired, evenly over the top of the tortilla. Roll up the tortilla, keeping the filling inside the tortilla as much as possible. Repeat with the remaining ingredients.

Day 102
Build a City

Materials:
Assorted wood scraps
Saw
Sandpaper
Waterproof glue
Permanent markers or paint

Directions: Look at the wood pieces you have collected. Do some of the shapes already look like buildings or parts of buildings? Glue the wood pieces with waterproof glue. Let dry. Paint the houses and shops. Add details with the permanent markers.

Day 103

Attach a postcard of your city with a message to a balloon and let the balloon fly.

Day 104

Overflowing Rice Trick

Materials:
Two identical empty margarine tubs with lids
Scissors
Glue
Tape
A cup of uncooked rice
A deep-sided tray
Colored paper or paints

Preparation: Carefully cut around the lip of one of the margarine tub lids, leaving an edge so that it can be glued easily. Glue the lid into one of the tubs, about halfway down.

Performance: Fill the unaltered tub above the brim with rice. Level this off with your magic wand, letting the rice spillage fall on the tray. Take the lid off the second tub, keeping the open top away from your audience. Place the changed tub upside down on top of the tub that is filled with rice. Turn the tubs sideways, holding them firmly together, and show them to all four corners of the room. When you turn to face your audience, turn the tubs upright onto the tray, making sure the altered tub is now at the bottom. As you dramatically removed the top tub, the rice will spill out all over the tray. The rice apparently doubled.

Day 105

Create Handmade Paper

Materials:
Used paper and scraps of all kinds, including office paper, colored construction paper, and wrapping paper

Blender
Dishpan or washtub
Window screen and matching picture frame small enough to fit inside the dishpan (or this can be bought in craft stores as a papermaker's mold and deckle set)
Sponge

Thick wool blanket or felt
Old sheet

Directions: Tear the paper into small pieces smaller than your fingers. The smaller the better. Place all the pieces into the blender until 3/4 full. Fill the blender with water almost to the top. Blend by pressing the pulse button on and off. When the pulp is ready to become paper, it will look as thick as stew. Fill the dishpan halfway to the top with water, then pour the paper pulp from blender into the dish pan until 3/4 full. Hold the frame on top of the screen and dip them together into the pulp. Shake the screen gently back and forth to spread the pulp evenly over the surface of the screen. Keep the screen and the frame level so the paper will have an even thickness. Use a sponge or your hands to squeeze the water out of pulp. When water completely drips out, remove pulp from mold. Quickly and steadily flip over the screen onto the blanket or felt and press the back of the screen with your fingers to release the paper onto the blanket or felt. Place the sheet over the fresh paper and press to get more of the water out of the pulp. Flip over the fabric, paper, and sheet sandwich so the sheet is on the bottom, and carefully peel the fabric from the paper. Place the sheet with the fresh paper on it in a safe place to dry. When dry, you have a sheet of handmade paper.

Day 106

Lasers Science Experiment

In this experiment, see which wavelength of laser light are absorbed by some materials and not by others.

Materials:
Laser pointer
Red jelly dessert
Blue jelly dessert

Directions: Shine the laser pointer through a clear pan of red jelly dessert and another full of blue. See which color transmits or passes through, and which absorbs it.

Day 107

Almond Fruit Float from China

Ingredients:

1 envelope unflavored gelatin   1/2 cup milk
1 cup water   1 tablespoon almond extract
1/2 cup sugar   1 13-ounce can fruit with syrup

Directions: In a saucepan, dissolve gelatin in water. Place over high heat and bring to a boil. Then reduce heat to low. Add sugar and stir until thoroughly dissolved. Stir in milk and almond extract. Mix well. Pour into a deep, square pan and allow to set at room temperature. Then put in refrigerator to cool. When cool, cut into cubes and serve topped with fruit and syrup. (If there is not enough syrup with the fruit, make a syrup by mixing 1 cup of water with 3 tablespoons sugar and 1/4 teaspoon almond extract in a small pan. Warm over low heat, stirring, until sugar is dissolved. Chill and serve with fruit and gelatin.)

Day 108

Magazine Box

Materials:

Box that matches the height of your magazines
Scissors
Tape
Pen
Wrapping paper

Directions: On your box, draw a strong dotted diagonal line halfway across the side of the box to mark where you will cut the box. Using kitchen scissors, cut all the way around the lines including the top of the box. Cover the box in wrapping paper. Trim paper before folding it over the edges. Tape the paper down inside and underneath.

Day 109

Fly a Kite

Day 110

Lemon Yogurt Cookies

Ingredients:

1 egg   1/4 cup packed brown sugar
1 teaspoon vanilla   1/2 cup granulated sugar
1/4 cup margarine   1/4 cup shortening
1 1/4 cups all-purpose flour   3/4 teaspoon salt
1/2 teaspoon baking soda   1/2 cup lemon yogurt
1/2 cup chopped toasted almonds   1/4 cup lemon yogurt
2 cups sifted powdered sugar

Directions: In a mixer bowl cream together sugars, margarine, shortening, egg, vanilla, 1/2 cup lemon yogurt and almonds (save some almonds for topping). Stir together flour, salt, and baking soda; stir into creamed mixture. Blend well. Drop from a teaspoon 2 inches apart onto a greased cookie sheet. Bake in a 375° oven for 8 to 10 minutes. Let stand 30 seconds. Remove from cookie sheet to a wire rack. Cool. Frost with a mixture of sifted powdered sugar and 1/4 cup lemon yogurt. Sprinkle with remaining chopped toasted almonds. Makes 3 dozen cookies.

Day 111

Chocolate-Peanut Crinkles

Ingredients:

1 egg   1/4 cup packed brown sugar
1 teaspoon vanilla   1/2 cup granulated sugar
1/4 cup margarine   1/4 cup shortening
1 cup all-purpose flour   3/4 teaspoon salt
1/2 teaspoon baking soda   1/2 cup chopped peanuts
11/2 squares unsweetened melted chocolate, cooled

Directions: In a mixer bowl cream together sugars, margarine, shortening, egg, vanilla, peanuts, and chocolates. Stir together flour, salt, and baking soda; stir into creamed mixture. Blend well. Drop from a teaspoon 2 inches apart onto a greased cookie sheet. Bake in a 375° oven for 8 to 10 minutes. Let stand 30 seconds. Remove from cookie sheet to a wire rack. Cool. Makes 3 dozen cookies.

Day 112
Read a Book to an Elderly Person at the Retirement Home

Day 113
Organize your room today!

Day 114
Nature Mobile

Materials:
Bark, Bones, Seashells, Leaves, 2 sticks, twine

Directions: Take a nature walk in a group or with a family member or friend. Collect things from that walk. Then cross and tie the 2 sticks together with twine for the mobile. Tie desired length of twine from center top of mobile for hanger. Tie each piece of your collection to the hanger with a piece of twine. Make sure everything is balanced so the mobile will hang level.

Day 115
Perky Pens

Materials:
Ballpoint pens, chenille stems, balls, beads, fabric trims, floral tape in green, hot-glue/glue sticks

Directions: Beginning at writing end of pen, wrap tape around pen. Make certain to cover pen completely. Glue decorative element to end of pen.

Day 116
Take an acting class!

Day 117

Disappearing Wand Magic Trick

In this trick, the audience see a wand disappear up your nose.

Materials:
Black construction paper
White construction paper
Glue
Scissors

Preparation: Roll up a piece of black paper to make a narrow tube about 6"
long. Then stick down the edge. Cut a piece of white paper 1/2" x 2". Wrap
it around one end of the tube and glue it in place. Wrap more white paper 3/4"
x 2 1/4" around the other end. This must be loose enough to slide up and
down. Glue down the edge.

Performance: Place the fixed end of the wand against your nose with the white
hidden beneath your fingers. Keeping the other white end in view, slide it slowly up the tube. As you move the sliding white end up toward your nose, keep
the protruding black end hidden behind your hand. Slide the white end back to
its starting position, take the wand away, and show that your nose and the
wand are just fine.

Day 118

Make a Tropical Snow Globe

Materials:
One 16-oz glass jar with a screw-on lid (pickle jars are ideal)
Plastic figures and toys that fit inside the jar
Silicone adhesive
Sand or small pebbles
2 ounces of glycerin
Liquid measuring cup
14 oz of water
Eyedropper
Glitter
Teaspoon

Directions: Set the jar lid upside down and arrange your figures and toys in place on the inside of the lid. Make sure the glass jar will fit over your scene once the cap is completely screwed on. Squeeze some of the silicone adhesive onto the jar lid and stick the plastic figures on the adhesive. Sprinkle sand, glitter, or pebbles over the sticky silicone adhesive. Let the lid sit overnight so that adhesive has time to dry. When dry and firm, move everything to a sink and fill the jar with water and the glycerin. Add about a teaspoon of glitter to the jar for the "snow" and fill jar completely so there are no air bubbles in the snow globe. Cap your jar. Guide the tops of the figures on the jar lid through the mouth of the jar and into the water mixture. Screw the lid on evenly and tightly. It's now complete.

Day 119

Touchscreen Science Experiment

In this experiment, see which objects conduct or pass along the electric current and trigger the screen

Materials:
Touchscreen in the community (banks, kiosks, theaters, supermarkets, etc.)
Banana
Cardboard
Metal spoon
Plastic spoon

Directions: Using each object, test to see which ones actually conducts electric current and triggers the screen.

Day 120

Pineapple-Coconut Cookies

Ingredients:

1 egg	1/4 cup packed brown sugar
1 teaspoon vanilla	1/2 cup granulated sugar
1/4 cup margarine	1/4 cup shortening
1 1/4 cups all-purpose flour	3/4 teaspoon salt
1/4 teaspoon ground ginger	1/2 cup well-drained crushed pineapple
1 cup flaked coconut	1/2 cup chopped walnuts

Directions: In a mixer bowl cream together sugars, margarine, shortening, egg, vanilla. Stir together flour, salt, ginger, coconut, walnuts, pineapple, and baking soda; stir into creamed mixture. Blend well. Drop from a teaspoon 2 inches apart onto a greased cookie sheet. Bake in a 375° oven for 8 to 10 minutes. Let stand 30 seconds. Remove from cookie sheet to a wire rack. Cool. Makes 31/2 dozen cookies.

Day 121

Make an African Drum

Materials:
Oatmeal box
Brown felt
Yarn
Poster paints
Paintbrush
Paper punch or a sharp pencil
Scissors

Directions: Paint an oatmeal box and its cover with a dark color. Cut out two felt circles that are larger than the top of the box. Punch an equal number of holes around the edge of the felt circles with a paper punch or with a sharp pencil. Place a felt circle on the bottom and top of the box. Tie one end of a long piece of yarn into one hole on the bottom circle of felt and knot it. Bring the yarn up to a hole on the top felt circle, and push the yarn through. Move the yarn down through another hole in the bottom circle and then up through a hole into the top circle. Continue this process until you have gone completely around the box, filling all the holes of the felt circles with the yarn lacing. If you need more yarn to finish the drum, tie an extra piece to the yarn already used. Glue feathers to the top side of the drum.

Day 122

Write a congratulations card to a friend who have a recent success

Day 123

Film Canister Mini-Lights

Materials:
Indoor use mini-lights
While or clear plastic film canisters
Drill with assorted bits
Several sheets of colored tissue paper
Pencil
Scissors
Ruler
Decoupage glue
1/2-inch-wide paintbrush
Hot glue gun and glue sticks

Directions: Have enough canisters for each light on the strand. Have an adult help drill holes in the bottom of each of the canisters. The hole should be large enough so that the light fits through the hole. If it doesn't, make the hole wider with a slightly larger drill bit. Trace the bottom of the canister with the hole on the tissue paper for each of the canisters. Then cut the tissue paper into strips that are roughly 2 inches wide and 4 1/2 inches long to wrap around the canisters. Make 2 strips for every canister. Use the paintbrush to spread a layer of the decoupage glue over the outside of the canister. Wrap a strip of the colored tissue paper around the canister, above the rim, and use your fingertips to smooth out any air bubbles or wrinkles between the paper and the canister. After wrapping all the canisters this same way, glue a second layer o paper around each one. Glue the paper circles to the outside bottoms of the canisters. Smooth out any air bubbles or wrinkles as you press each paper circle in place. Brush a final coat of the decoupage glue over the outsides of the canisters and just inside the rims to seal the paper layers. Push each canister over a mini-light so the base of the light fits in the canister hole. Use your new mini-lights to decorate your room, bathroom, bulletin board, anything. Remember to unplug after a couple of hours and after you leave your room.

Day 124

Make a Yo-Yo

Materials:
Model Magic (from art supply stores)
2-foot string
Paint

Directions: Roll the Model Magic into a round ball about the size of your palm. Slice two lines around the sphere, as far apart as your pinkie. Gently pull out the slice, leaving room for the string to be wound. Let dry, and paint using bright colors and your own design. Tie on the string.

Day 125

Cereal Magic Trick

In this trick, when you open a box of cereal in front of an audience and pour, only 1 cereal flake comes out. You show the audience the box is empty by opening the bottom and allowing the audience to look right through it. When you close the bottom and the top and tap your wand on the box, you can pour a full portion of cereal into the bowl.

Materials:
2 identical cereal boxes
Bowlful of cereal
Glue
Scissors
Velcro
A Bowl
A Spoon

Preparation: Open the flaps of both boxes. Cut a section out of on box, going from the bottom corner to a width of 1 1/2 in. at the top. Turn the section inside out and spread glue on its outside edges. Stick it firmly inside the uncut cereal box. Cut two strips of Velcro and glue them to the bottom flaps of the box. Now close the box at the bottom and fasten. Pour the cereal into the secret compartment. Cover the cereal with one of the side flaps and try shaking the box. Make sure it is pack so it doesn't rattle. Close the box.

Performance: Open the cereal box and pour the single cereal flake into the bowl. Look sad when you see that there is nothing left. Open up the bottom flaps of the cereal box and pointing the base toward the audience, show them that the box is empty. Close the flaps of the cereal box and tap the box with your magic wand. Now open the top of the box and pour out a whole bowlful of cereal.

Day 126

Take a dance class!

Day 127

Colorful Collection Boxes

Materials:
2 empty cereal boxes
Scissors
Ruler
Pencil
Glue
Paint
Brush
Decorations

Directions: Mark an X across an empty cereal box. Measure the depth of the box. Draw a border that is the same width as the box's depth. Cut along the X lines to open up the center of the box. Cut away the center panel – you will be left with a flap on each side. Fold the flaps neatly down inside the box and glue them into position. Hold them in place until they are completely dry. For the shelves, make dividers that run the height and width of the box. For extra strength, cut them twice as wide as the depth of the box. Fold the pieces of cardboard over and glue them down. They must be slotted together to go in the box, so mark the intersections and cut the slits. Paint the dividers and then slot them together. Paint or wrap the box. Glue the back and side edges of the dividers and push them into the box. Paint the entire box. Wait for the paint to dry. Glue decorations around the box. Then display small souvenirs or objects in the box.

Day 128

Chocolate-Topped Peppermint Cookies

Materials:

3/4 cup granulated sugar   1/4 cup margarine, softened
1 egg   2 tablespoons milk
1 1/4 cups all-purpose flour   1 tablespoon boiling water
1/2 teaspoon baking soda   1/2 teaspoon salt
1/4 teaspoon peppermint extract   1/2 ounce unsweetened chocolate
1 tablespoon margarine   1/2 cup sifted powdered sugar
1/4 teaspoon vanilla   1/2 cup chopped walnuts

Directions: In a mixer bowl cream together sugar and margarine. Beat in egg, milk, peppermint extract, and margarine. Stir together flour, baking soda, walnuts, and salt. Add to creamed mixture; mix just till blended. Spread in a greased 9x9x2-inch baking pan. Bake in a 375° oven for 17 to 20 minutes. Remove. While bars are still slightly warm, drizzle with Chocolate Glaze: In a small saucepan melt chocolate, 1 tablespoon margarine. Stir in sifted powdered sugar and vanilla till crumbly. Blend in enough boiling water to achieve pouring consistency. Makes 2 dozen bars.

Day 129

Toss Some Stars

Create a soft Star-shape bean bag

Materials:
Yellow felt, about 1/4 yard
Dried beans, peas, or rice
Needle and thread

Directions: Sketch the outline of a star on a piece of paper. Make the outline about 1/2" bigger than you want the final beanbag to be. Cut out the star shape. Fold the felt in half and pin the paper shape to it. Cut around the paper. Remove the paper pattern and stitch the two felt pieces together with small even stitches (leave a 1/2" seam allowance). Leave a 2" opening in the bag. Turn the fabric right side out. Fill the star with beans, then sew the opening shut. Now you have a star you can toss or use as a paperweight.

Day 130

Go Skateboarding

Day 131

Punch-art Cards

Materials:
Assorted card stocks, assorted craft punches, assorted decorative paper, decorative-edged scissors, glue stick, hole punch, paper cutter ribbons.

Directions: Using paper cutter, cut card stocks into various sizes. Fold in half for cards. Trim decorative paper so that it is slightly smaller than card front. Glue decorative papers onto cards. Using craft punches, punch out shapes from decorative papers. Glue onto cards. Using hole punch, punch hole in top folded corner of card and thread with ribbon.

Day 132

Ice Cream Sandwiches

From 1 to a group of 30 people

Ingredients:
low-fat oatmeal cookies, chocolate chip cookies, peanut butter cookies or any kind of large cookies, light vanilla ice cream, sprinkles in a shallow bowl, water

Directions: Put the cookies side by side, with the flat side facing up, on a plate in front of him or her. Using an ice-cream scoop, scoop out the ice cream. Place the scoop on one of the cookies and press down on it with a large spoon or spatula to flatten out the ice cream. Place the second cookie on top of the ice cream, flat side down. Roll the ice-cream sandwich in the sprinkles to decorate the sides.

Day 133

Happy Daisy Picture Frame

Materials:
Cardboard
Ruler
Pencil
String
Tape
Craft Glue
Green Fake Fur
Light Fabric Daisies

Directions: Measure out a frame on a large sheet of cardboard. Make it wide enough – about 3 inches to create a design. Cut out the frame using a ruler and craft knife. Keep the middle window smaller than the picture to be framed. Tape string to the back, or if the frame is heavy, knot string through holes in the cardboard. Spread craft glue on the cardboard. Stick the cardboard to the fake fur. Trim the corners of the fur. Cut an X in the fabric inside the frame; then trim the fabric and glue it in place. Attach string and decorate. Glue the daisies to the front of the frame.

Day 134

Visit the local zoo or animal park.

Day 135

Start a Pet Sitting Service

If you are good with pets and are responsible, you can offer your neighbors a pet sitting service whenever they go on vacation. Decide how much you are going to charge for your pet sitting service. Then advertise it to your neighbors.

Day 136

Learn How to Do a Western Dance

Day 137
Go Body Painting

Materials:
Muffin tin or small paper cups
6 teaspoons cornstarch
3 teaspoons cold cream
Food coloring
Small paintbrushes

Directions: Mix 1 teaspoon cornstarch, 1/2 teaspoon water, and a few drops of food coloring to create each color in its own cup. Stir well, then dip your brush in and start painting.

Day 138
Learn to Whistle or Play the Harmonica

Day 139
Fudge-Almond Bonbons

Ingredients:

Margarine	2 cups sugar
3/4 cup milk	2 squares (2 ounces) unsweetened chocolate
1 tablespoon light corn syrup	dash of salt
2 tablespoons margarine	1 pound confectioners' coating
32 unblanched whole almonds	
1 teaspoon vanilla	
or 1/2 teaspoon almond extract	

Directions: Butter a 9x5x3-inch loaf pan. Butter the sides of a heavy-gauge 2-quart saucepan. Clip a candy thermometer to side of pan. In the saucepan, stir together the sugar, milk, chocolate, corn syrup, and salt. Cook and stir over medium heat till sugar is dissolved and mixture begins to boil. Stir gently to avoid splashing syrup on sides of pan, which causes candy to become grainy. The mixture will begin to bubble vigorously and will rise close to pan rim. Use medium rather than high heat to prevent the mixture from sticking or boiling over.

Continue cooking the mixture, stirring only as necessary to prevent sticking, to 234° or the softball stage (a few drops of the mixture, dropped from a teaspoon into cold water, form a soft ball that flattens when removed from the water). Watch closely; temperature rises quickly above 220°.

Immediately remove pan from heat; add the 2 tablespoons margarine but do not stir. Cool mixture, without stirring or moving pan, till thermometer registers 110°, or till bottom of pan feels comfortably warm to the touch. Stirring or moving the mixture can result in grainy candy.

Remove the thermometer. Stir in vanilla; beat mixture by hand with a wooden spoon, lifting candy with an up-and-over motion, till mixture becomes thick, starts to lose its gloss, and doesn't stream back into the pan when the spoon is lifted (or, till the mixture holds its shape when dropped onto waxed paper). Stir in peanut butter; swirl once or twice to marble. Do not use an electric mixer.

Immediately spread fudge in the buttered pan. Cool; cut into squares.

In a double boiler over hot, not boiling, water, melt 1 pound confectioners' coating. For each bonbon, hold one square at a time on a fork over confectioners' coating; spoon melted coating over fudge, covering all sides. Place candy on waxed paper or foil; top each piece with a whole unblanched almond. Allow pieces to dry; store in a covered container between layers of waxed paper. Store candy in cool place. Makes 32 pieces.

Day 140

Take a self-defense class such as karate, judo, or kung fu.

Day 141

Toast some Marshmallows

Day 142

The Story of My Family

Materials:
A journal or notebook

Directions: Interview everyone in your family, creating a chapter for each member. Then write a chapter on the following:

Things that matters to us
Family recipes
Where our ancestors lived
What did our ancestors do
What our grandparent's lives were like when they were our age
Things our family do when we are together
Traditions and stories that were passed down
Our family celebrations

Day 143

Colonial Apple Butter Gifts

Ingredients:
41/2 cups apple cider
14 cups coarsely chopped apples (core apples, pare, cut into wedges, then into smaller pieces)
1/2 cup maple syrup
1 teaspoon ground cinnamon
1/2 teaspoon ground cloves
1/2 teaspoon allspice

Directions: With adult supervision, pour the cider into a large cooking pot. Let the cider boil 15 minutes. Add the apple pieces to the cider. Reduce the heat to a simmer and cook, covered, until tender, 1 hour, stirring the apples every 15 minutes. Remove the pot from the heat and mash the apples with a potato masher. Stir in the maple syrup, cinnamon, cloves, and allspice. Cook the apple mixture over low heat, uncovered, stirring often, until it thickens, about 30 minutes. Turn off the heat and let the apple butter cool for 15 minutes.

Wash glass jars in hot, soapy water, rinse in hot water, then let drain on a dishtowel while the apple butter cools. Then spoon the apple butter carefully into the jars. Store the apple butter in the refrigerator and give away to friends and neighbors.

Day 144

Pigs in a Blanket

Materials:
1 11-ounce pop-can of refrigerated soft breadstick dough (for 8 breadsticks)
8 light or low-fat hot dogs
Ketchup or mustard for dipping

Makes 8 servings

Directions: Preheat oven to 350°F. Break open the pop-can and separate the breadstick dough into 8 pieces. Wrap a piece of breadstick dough around each hot dog. Either make a spiral around the frank or mush the dough together and form it around the frank like a corn dog. Place the breaded franks on a non-stick baking sheet. Have an adult cook the breaded franks in the center of the oven for 15 to 18 minutes or until the breadstick dough is lightly browned.

Day 145

Window Art

Materials: Study cardboard, about 20" x 30"
Colored pencils, markers, or paint
Yardstick or long ruler

Directions: Draw the outlines of the window frame on the cardboard. Match the size and style of those windows near where you will hang the painting, or make the window any way you like. Draw the bottom half of the window as it might look if viewed from above to give the illusion of depth. Pencil in the landscape or outdoor scene as it would be seen from the window. Color in the painting. Paint the window frame with two shades of the same color. Use the darker shade to suggest shadows cast by the frame. Make the outdoor scene lighter in color so it appears to be in the distance. Draw an object on the windowsill such as a cat or a potted plant. Paint this object, paying special attention to how it would look lit with the bright light from the window. Last, hang the picture level with the other windows in the room or at a logical height.

Jackie

Note from Jackie:
Go at Your Own Pace!
Enjoy the time you take to do these activities.

Day 146
Candy Tin Travel Games

Materials:
Old magazines or books
Use of a photocopy machine
Scissors
Metal candy tin
100-grit sandpaper
3-D paint
Acrylic paints and paintbrush
Newspapers
Clear acrylic spray enamel
Self-adhesive magnetic sheets
Tweezers

Directions: Collect words by photocopy text from books or cut words from the pages of old magazines. Use the 100-grit sandpaper to scrub the old paint off of the candy tin. Draw a border around the lit with the 3-D paint, and decorate the tin with acrylic paint. Set the tin on newspapers outdoors, and spray it with the clear acrylic enamel. This prevents the new paint from chipping. Peel the paper backing off of the magnetic sheet and set the sheet down so the sticky side faces up. Use the tweezers to life the words you've cut out and stick them to the magnetic sheet. Cut the words from the magnetic sheet and store them in the tin. You can also make checkers or chess versions.

Day 147
Have a Circus Parade in your Backyard

Day 148

Create a Gifted Girls® Rose Boa

Materials:
Feather fabric
Thin plastic party tablecloths at 84" round
Old pair of panty hose
Sequins
Bells,
Ribbons
Feathers
Lace

Directions: Choose the material you would use for your boa. Cut the material into feather strips that are approximately 1" wide x 8" long and set aside. Cut the top off a pair of panty hose about 5" down from the waistband. Discard the top part. Spread the panty hose legs apart so that the toes are at opposite ends. Tie each toe to something sturdy at either end, making sure the panty hose are stretched out as much as possible. Now you're ready to tie on your feathers. Start at one end of the stretched panty hose and tie on a feather strip with a tight knot, keeping the ends even. Continue to add strips, tying each one as close to the next as possible. Every few ties, push the tied strips tightly together and twirl them around so they fluff out evenly and the ends aren't all pointing in the same direction. When the boa is complete, untie the panty hose toes and make a big double knot at each end so the strips won't fall off. Cut off the excess toe on each end. Decorate by tying the ribbons, bells and feathers on.

Day 149

Visit an Ice Cream Factory

Day 150
Caramel Apples

Ingredients:
6 crisp, juicy medium-size apples
6 wooden sticks
1 14-ounce package caramels
2 tablespoons water

Directions: Peel the wrappers off each caramel and place the caramels in a 2- or
–4-cup glass measure (or microwave-safe bowl of similar shape). Add the 2
tablespoons of water to the measuring cup with the caramels and microwave on
HIGH about 3 minutes or until smooth, stirring after each minute. Let the
caramel sauce stand a few minutes to cool slightly. Dip the apples in the
caramel while holding onto the stick. Spread and even out the caramel once
you pull the apple out of the caramel sauce using a wooden stick as a knife.
Scrape off excess sauce from the bottom of the apple using the wooden stick.
Place the caramel apples on greased wax paper. Store in the refrigerator for up
to two days. Before serving let stand at room temperature 15 minutes to soften
the caramel a little.

Day 151
Visit a Fish Farm

Day 152
Plant an Avocado Tree

Materials: Avocado Seed
Toothpicks
Glass
Water

Directions: Stick toothpicks into the avocado seed evenly spaced out. Fill glass
with water so that it covers the bottom of the seed when the seed is placed on
top of the glass. The seed is held up by the toothpicks. Leave this avocado
plant by a window or sunny spot and make sure the water keeps touching the
bottom of the seed. Soon, the avocado seed will sprout, and you will be able to
plant an avocado tree.

Day 153

Make a Desk Blotter

Materials:
Large cardboard
Fabric
Acrylic plastic
Glue
Staple

Directions: Cut 2 inch strips from the sides of the large cardboard. Cut (2) 2 1/2" strips from the fabric. Cover the fabric over the cardboard and staple underneath. Cover the cardboard strips in fabric and staple underneath. Take Glue one strip on top of the edge of one side. Glue the other strip to the edge of the other side. Cut the acrylic plastic to fit in between the two edges.

Day 154

Banana Magic Trick

In this magic trick, an audience member choose a number, and as a banana is peeled, the banana breaks up into the same number of pieces as the number chosen by your audience.

Materials:
Stiff paper or cardboard
A thick pen
Scissors
A bunch of bananas
A darning needle

Preparation: Cut out four pieces of cardboard about the same size as playing cards. Write a number on each card. Choose any numbers, but one of them must be a 3. Right before the performance, but not so early that the banana will turn brown, stick the darning needle into one of the bananas a third of the way to the top. Wiggle the needle gently from side to side. In the same way, make a second hole with the needle a third of the way from the bottom of the banana.

Performance: Put the four cards face up on the table, in no particular order. Then ask your helper to choose any two numbers. If your helper has not picked the 3, take away the two cards he has picked. If he has picked the 3 as one of his two cards, take the other two cards off the table. You need to be left with the 3 on the table. Ask your helper to pick one of the two remaining cards. You need to be left with the 3 on the table. If he has pointed to the 3, take away the other card. If he has not pointed to the 3, take away the card he has pointed to. Hand your helper a banana and tell your helper that the banana will indicate which number he has chosen. Tell your helper to peel the banana. The banana will fall into three pieces.

Day 155

Sand Dried Flowers

Materials:
Cardboard box
Sand
Scissors
Freshly picked flowers
Drinking straws or florist sticks
Beading wire (purchasable in five-and-ten cent stores) or pipe cleaners
Green construction paper
Liquid white glue

Directions: Fill the cardboard box half-full with sand. Cut away most of the stem from each flower. The remaining stem should be as long as your middle finger. Push the stem of each flower into the sand. Sprinkle a thin layer of sand over the flowers making sure to cover them completely. If you have a thick flower with many petals, such as a rose, open the petals slightly, and fill in the spaces between the petals with sand. Place the box in a dry place like a closet or an attic. Let the flowers dry in the sand for two weeks. When the flowers have dried, carefully tilt the box and pour out the top sand. Carefully lift out the flowers. Florists sell green wooden sticks that can be used as stems for your flowers. You can also use drinking straws. Carefully attach flowers to the stems with beading wire or pipe cleaners. Cut out leaves from green construction paper. Glue the leaves to the stems of the flowers.

Day 156

Flower Paperweights

Materials:
Glass ashtray or small jar with a lid
Colored construction paper
Pencil
Scissors
Liquid white glue
Sand-dried flowers (Day 157)
Waxed Paper

Directions: Turn the ashtray upside down and place it on a sheet of colored construction paper. Trace around the edge with a pencil. Cut out the tracing with scissors. Glue one or several of the sand-dried flowers on the cutout tracing. Let the glue dry completely on the paper. Place the paper with the flower on top of a piece of waxed paper, which will protect your working surface. Squeeze liquid white glue along the edges of the construction paper cutout. Fit the upside down ashtray onto the wet glue, matching the shape of the ashtray to that of the paper as exactly as you can. Allow the paperweight to dry completely before you handle it. Or, if you are using a jar with a lid, proceed as follows: Glue the flower to the inside of the jar lid. When the flower has dried in place, carefully screw the jar onto the lid.

Day 157

Signature Colorful Ombre Scarf

Materials:
Clothesline and clothespins
Newspapers
White or off-white silk scarf
Water
Mild detergent
Large stainless steel pot
Rubber gloves
1 package powdered Rit or Tintex dye
Measuring spoons
Large metal spoon
Large metal mixing bowl or plastic bin
Old towel or washing machine

Directions: Hang a clothesline over a thick stack of newspapers in a safe spot near where you will be dyeing. Wash the silk scarf in hot water with mild detergent. Rinse well. Fill the pot with 2 gallons of water and heat the water to near boiling with adult supervision. Turn off the stove. Put on your rubber gloves. Add 1/2 teaspoon of the powdered dye to the pot and mix well with the metal spoon. Begin dyeing with a small amount of dye for the lightest color and add more as you go along to get darker and darker shades. Plan to dip your scarf in four sections; each section will be a slightly darker shade of the same color. Place the first quarter of the silk scarf in the dye-bath and allow it to sit for thirty minutes. Remove the scarf and squeeze out excess dye. Place the dyed end of the scarf in a metal bowl or plastic bin so that it doesn't drip as you carry it. Hang it on the drying line until you're ready to move on to the next dipping. Add another teaspoon of dye to the same pot and stir. Next dip all but the dyed quarter of the scarf into the dye, and swish it around so it's thoroughly soaked. Leave it in for 30 minutes, then remove the scarf and squeeze out excess dye.

Hang it on the drying line until it's ready to be dipped again. Add another tea-spoon of dye to the pot and mix well. Dip only the third and fourth quarters of the scarf in the pot, soaking thoroughly. Leave it in for 30 minutes, then remove the scarf and squeeze out excess dye. Hang it on the drying line until it's ready to be dipped again. Mix 1 more teaspoon of dye into the pot, and dip only the last quarter of the scarf into the dye; let it sit for 30 minutes. When dyeing is complete, rinse the scarf thoroughly under cold running water. Keep the light and dark ends of the scarf from touching each other. Fill your plastic bucket or metal bowl with cold water and a dash of mild detergent, and swish the scarf around for 5 minutes. Rinse the scarf in cold water and squeeze out excess water. Squeeze the scarf in an old towel and put it in the washer on spin cycle by itself. Hang the scarf and let it dry thoroughly. If you use the washer, remember to run the washer again to clean out excess dye before your next load of laundry.

Day 159

Visit a Candy Factory

Day 159

Signature Sugar Magic Trick

In this magic trick, a letter appears magically on an audience member's hand.

Materials:
A cube of sugar.
Pencil
Glass of water

Preparation: Write a letter on the sugar cube and touch the letter with a finger.

Performance: Hold the cup of water and drop the sugar cube in, saying, "sugar melt." Then say, "magic letter float up." Get an audience member to cover the glass with his palm by showing him what to do. Hold the hand of the audience member and touch the finger with the letter to his palm. Have him cover the glass. The letter should appear on his palm when he removes it from the glass.

Day 160

Coconut Shell Bowl

Materials:
A fresh coconut
Sandpaper

Directions: Have an adult cut the coconut in half into two perfectly round bowls. Bake the coconut halves at 300° F in an oven for 10 minutes or until you can easily remove the nutmeat from the shell. Use the sandpaper to smooth the outside of the shell. Wash and dry inside and outside.

Day 161

Have a Hula Hoop Contest

Day 162
Root Beer Float

Ingredients:
Root beer
2 Scoops low-fat vanilla ice cream or frozen yogurt

Directions: Slowly add the root beer to the ice cream or frozen yogurt. Stir slightly so flavors mix.

Day 163
Start a Kids' Clean-up Club to keep your Neighborhood Clean!

Day 164
German Chocolate Fudge

Ingredients:

Margarine	1 3/4 cups sugar
3/4 cup milk	3 squares (3 ounces) sweet chocolate
1 tablespoon light corn syrup	dash of salt
1 teaspoon vanilla	2 tablespoons margarine
1/2 cup chopped pecans	1/3 cup toasted coconut

Directions: Butter a 9x5x3-inch loaf pan. Butter the sides of a heavy-gauge 2-quart saucepan. Clip a candy thermometer to side of pan. In the saucepan, stir together the sugar, milk, chocolate, corn syrup, and salt. Cook and stir over medium heat till sugar is dissolved and mixture begins to boil. Stir gently to avoid splashing syrup on sides of pan, which causes candy to become grainy. The mixture will begin to bubble vigorously and will rise close to pan rim. Use medium rather than high heat to prevent the mixture from sticking or boiling over.

Continue cooking the mixture, stirring only as necessary to prevent sticking, to 234° or the softball stage (a few drops of the mixture, dropped from a teaspoon into cold water, form a soft ball that flattens when removed from the water).

Watch closely; temperature rises quickly above 220°.

Immediately remove pan from heat; add the 2 tablespoons margarine but do not stir. Cool mixture, without stirring or moving pan, till thermometer registers 110°, or till bottom of pan feels comfortably warm to the touch. Stirring or moving the mixture can result in grainy candy.

Remove the thermometer. Stir in vanilla; beat mixture by hand with a wooden spoon, lifting candy with an up-and-over motion, till mixture becomes thick, starts to lose its gloss, and doesn't stream back into the pan when the spoon is lifted (or, till the mixture holds its shape when dropped onto waxed paper). Stir in pecans. Do not use an electric mixer.

Pour beaten fudge into the loaf pan. Sprinkle coconut evenly atop, pressing in gently with hands. Cool; cut into squares. Store in a tightly covered container in a cool place. Makes about 40 pieces.

Day 165
Heads Up for a Headband

Materials:
Felt strip or colorful ribbon (about 1" x 16")
Assorted felt scraps
Sequins, buttons and other trims
3/4" elastic, about 4" long
White glue
Needle and thread

Directions: Cut the felt scraps into various shapes. Glue them to one side of the long strip, using the glue sparingly, so that it doesn't bleed through the felt. Sew on other trims such as fabric trims, sequins, buttons, and beads. Sew the elastic on the inside of the headband at both ends.

Day 166
Sound Effects Studio

Crackling Fire
Materials: Crinkly plastic wrap.
Directions: Bunch up plastic wrap to make the sound of fire crackling.

Horses' Hooves
Materials: 2 plastic yogurt containers without lids.
Directions: Clap the open ends on a flat surface or over gravel to make hoof sounds, varying the speed for trotting, galloping or walking.

Ripping
Materials: 2 Velcro strips
Directions: Pull apart Velcro strips to make a ripping sound.

Train
Materials: Sandpaper, 2 cans, tape
Directions: Wrap sandpaper around each of the cans and tape in place. Rub the cans together to make a chugging train sound.

Rattlesnake
Materials: Dried peas, plastic water bottle
Directions: Put 1" of dry peas into a plastic water bottle. Hold at the top and shake to make a rattlesnake sound.

Crashing Sound
Materials: 2 cardboard boxes, metal pipes, cans, anything that make noise.
Directions: Put everything in one box, then pour the contents into the empty box to make a loud crashing sound.

Walking in the Snow
Materials: Box of cornstarch.
Directions: Squish a full cornstarch box hard with alternating thumbs in a walking rhythm.

Walking
Materials: Shoes with different type of soles.
Directions: Put your hands into old shoes and tap heel to toe, slowly for walking, faster for running. Walk on gravel or bread crumbs in a box to make crunchy sounds.

Rustling in the Bush
Materials: Bristle broom.
Directions: Hold a small bristle broom in one hand and twist the bristles to make the sound of something rustling in the bushes.

Day 167

Orange Creamsicle

Ingredients:
1 cup chilled orange juice
1 Scoops low-fat vanilla ice cream or frozen yogurt
7 ice cubes or chopped ice

Directions: Blend the orange juice and ice cream or frozen yogurt and ice cubes together.

Day 168

Learn Sign Language!

Day 169

Praline-Apple Crisp

Ingredients: 1 tablespoon water
1 teaspoon almond extract
6 cups sliced unpeeled tart eating apples (about 6 medium)
2 tablespoons firm margarine
2 tablespoons all-purpose flour
2 tablespoons packed brown sugar
1/2 teaspoon ground cinnamon
1/2 cup coarsely crushed zwieback cracker

2 tablespoons chopped pecans

Directions: Heat oven to 375°. Spray 1 1/2-quart casserole with nonstick cooking spray. Mix water and almond extract; toss with apples in casserole. Cut margarine into flour, brown sugar and cinnamon with pastry blender in small bowl until crumbly. Stir in zwieback and pecans. Sprinkle over apples. Bake uncovered about 30 minutes or until top is golden brown and apples are tender. Serve warm with a scoop of vanilla ice cream.

Day 170

Re-read your Favorite Gifted Girls Books!

Day 171

Grape Magic Trick

Materials:
2 small seedless grapes

Directions: Carefully place one of the grapes in your mouth, without your audience seeing you do it. It is crucial that the audience thinks you have only one grape. To begin this trick, pick up the remaining grape in your right hand. Show the grape to the audience, then pretend to place the grape in your left hand. Form a loose fist with your left hand to hide the grape that really is not there. Point to your left hand with the forefinger of your right hand. Try not to talk during this trick. The grape might pop out of your mouth! Put your left hand on the top of your head and pretend to squash the grape. Spreading your fingers as you press down make s it look as though you really have squashed the grape. Open your mouth to show the audience the grape inside it. If you did this joke convincingly, the audience will think the grape has moved through your head and into your mouth. Pretend to take the grape out of your mouth with your right hand. Then hold out your right hand and show the audience the grape that has been there since the beginning of the trick.

Day 172
Fudge S'Mores

Ingredients:

Margarine
3/4 cup milk
1 tablespoon light corn syrup
1 teaspoon vanilla
9 graham crackers
1/2 cup chopped walnuts

2 cups sugar
2 squares (2 ounces) unsweetened chocolate
dash of salt
2 tablespoons margarine
1 cup tiny marshmallows

Directions: Place 9 graham crackers in the bottom of a foil-lined 8x8x2-inch pan, cutting crackers if necessary to fit. Sprinkle 1 cup tiny marshmallows evenly over crackers.

Clip a candy thermometer to side of pan. In the saucepan, stir together the sugar, milk, chocolate, corn syrup, and salt. Cook and stir over medium heat till sugar is dissolved and mixture begins to boil. Stir gently to avoid splashing syrup on sides of pan, which causes candy to become grainy. The mixture will begin to bubble vigorously and will rise close to pan rim. Use medium rather than high heat to prevent the mixture from sticking or boiling over.

Continue cooking the mixture, stirring only as necessary to prevent sticking, to 234° or the softball stage (a few drops of the mixture, dropped from a teaspoon into cold water, form a soft ball that flattens when removed from the water). Watch closely; temperature rises quickly above 220°.

Immediately remove pan from heat; add the 2 tablespoons margarine but do not stir. Cool mixture, without stirring or moving pan, till thermometer registers 110°, or till bottom of pan feels comfortably warm to the touch. Stirring or moving the mixture can result in grainy candy.

Remove the thermometer. Stir in vanilla; beat mixture by hand with a wooden spoon, lifting candy with an up-and-over motion, till mixture becomes thick, starts to lose its gloss, and doesn't stream back into the pan when the spoon is lifted (or, till the mixture holds its shape when dropped onto waxed paper). Do not use an electric mixer.

Immediately pour beaten fudge evenly over marshmallow layer, spreading to cover completely. Sprinkle 1/2 cup chopped walnuts atop, pressing in with hands. Score; cut into squares when cool.   Store in a tightly covered container in a cool place. Makes about 36 pieces.

Day 173
Wild Bird Feeder

Materials:
Cord
Large pine cone
Spoon
Peanut butter
Birdseed
Waxed paper

Directions: Tie the cord to the top petals of the pine cone. Spoon peanut butter between the petals. Place birdseed on the waxed paper. Roll the peanut buttered pine cone in the birdseed. Hang the feeder in a tree.

Day 174
Milkshake

Ingredients:
2 Scoops low-fat vanilla ice cream or frozen yogurt
Chocolate milk

Directions: Mix all ingredients together in a blender for 15 seconds.

Day 175
Magical Hanky

Materials:
Handkerchief
Pencil

Directions: Curl the fingers of your left hand to make a tunnel. Position your hand so the tunnel runs up and down and lay the handkerchief over it. Push the handkerchief just slightly into the tunnel, using the forefinger of your right hand. Do not move your finger just yet. Use the middle finger of your right hand to push one edge of the handkerchief into the tunnel. You might have t open your left hand a little to do this. The audience must not see you making this gap between the handkerchief and your hand. Now pull your fingers out of the handkerchief. Pick up the pencil with your right hand and push it into the gap between the handkerchief and your left hand. Continue pushing the pencil until the pointed end can be seen coming out from under the handkerchief. Lay the pencil on the table and hold the handkerchief open so the audience can see that there is no hole in it.

Day 176
Learn to Juggle

Day 177
Puzzle of Nature

Materials:
Damaged or dying leaf.

Directions: Tear this leaf into many pieces (I suggest as many pieces as there are people playing). Then together, try to put the leaf back together.

Day 178

Learn to Snap your Fingers

Day 179
Chocolate Ice-Cream Soda

Ingredients:
Chocolate milk
2 Scoops low-fat vanilla or chocolate ice cream or frozen yogurt
Seltzer water
Whipped cream
Cherry

Directions: Add chocolate milk to fill a third of a tall glass. Add ice cream or frozen yogurt, and fill to the top with seltzer water. Stir once or twice, then add whipped cream and a cherry.

Day 180

Visit an Arboretum

Day 181

Mannequin

Materials:
Large mirror with cloth.

Directions: Cover the mirror with the cloth. Take turns with your friend in being a window display mannequin in front of the covered mirror. One person is the mannequin. The other person is the window designer. The window designer moves the arms, legs, head, and fingers to create a scene. After the mannequin is posed. Take off the cloth and see if the mannequin is surprised.

Day 182

Pink Cow Float

Ingredients:
Raspberry soda
2 Scoops low-fat vanilla ice cream or frozen yogurt

Directions: Slowly add the soda to the ice cream or frozen yogurt. Stir slightly so flavors mix.

Day 183

Strawberry-Chocolate Meringues

Ingredients:
3 egg whites
1/4 teaspoon cream of tartar
3/4 cup sugar
1 ounce unsweetened chocolate, coarsely grated
2 cups sliced strawberries (1 pint)
1 quart strawberry nonfat frozen yogurt

Directions: Heat oven to 275°. Line cookie sheet with cooking parchment paper or aluminum foil. Beat egg whites and cream of tartar in medium bowl until foamy. Beat in sugar, 1 tablespoon at a time; continue beating until stiff and glossy. Do not underbeat. Fold in chocolate. Drop meringue by 1/3 cupfuls onto cookie sheet. Shape into about 3-inch circles, building up sides. Bake 1 hour. Turn off the oven; leave meringues in oven with door closed 1 1/2 hours. Remove from oven. Cool completely at room temperature. Place strawberries in blender or food processor. Cover and blend until smooth. Fill each meringue with about 1/2 cup frozen yogurt. Top with strawberry mixture.

Day 184

Topsy-Turvey Pencil Magic

Materials:
Pencil without an eraser
Pencil sharpener
Detachable pencil eraser

Directions: Sharpen the blunt ends of the pencil with the pencil sharpener. Make sure that both ends of the pencil look the same. Put the detachable pencil eraser on one end of the pencil. Your pencil should look like an ordinary pencil. Hold the pencil in your left hand so the eraser is hidden. Make sure you have a firm hold on the eraser. Point to the sharpened end of the pencil with your right hand and say in a mysterious way, "This is a very strange pencil." Place your right hand around the pointed end of the pencil and pull the pencil away from your left hand. The eraser must stay hidden in your left hand. Curl the fingers of your left hand to make a tunnel. Draw the audience's attention to the pointed end of the pencil and say, "The pointed end of this pencil has magically moved to the other end!" Push the pencil into the tunnel you have made with your left hand. Make sure the pencil slides into the eraser. Keep pushing the pencil until it comes out the other side of the tunnel. Say to the audience, "Now look what has happened. The point has moved and there is an eraser on the other end of the pencil."

Day 185

Learn a New Language

Day 186
Pizza Pockets

Ingredients:
Olive oil nonstick cooking spray
Assorted healthy pizza fillings that you or your friends like: Zucchini (diced),
green onions (chopped), mushrooms (sliced), fresh tomatoes (chopped), red or
green or yellow bell peppers (finely chopped), olives (sliced), pineapple chunks,
lean ham (chopped), Canadian bacon (chopped), ground sirloin (cooked and
crumbled)

1 10-ounce pop-can refrigerated pizza crust dough
1/2 cup prepared marinara or spaghetti sauce, divided
1 cup grated low-moisture part-skim mozzarella, divided
Grated Parmesan cheese (optional)

Makes 4 pizza pockets

Directions: Preheat the oven to 425°F. Coat a cookie sheet with olive oil nonstick cooking spray. Chop and prepare the pizza fillings you decided on and
keep each filling separate in its own bowl or dish. Spread the pizza crust out
flat on a lightly floured cutting board or surface area. Using a circle about 51/2
inches in diameter (like the top of a pitcher or oatmeal container), press it into
the pizza dough to cut out a circle. Place the dough circle on the cookie sheet.
Cut out three circles. Then add the scraps together, roll out or press into the
fourth circle. Spread about 1/8 cup of the marinara sauce over the circle using a
spoon or 1/8-cup measure. Sprinkle about 3 tablespoons of the cheese over the
sauce. Have everyone dig into the assorted fillings and use a spoon to scoop
out some of each and sprinkle it over the cheese. Using a metal fork, seal the
top and bottom ends together. Spray the top of each pizza pocket with nonstick
cooking spray, and sprinkle some Parmesan cheese over the top if desired. Bake
for about 15 minutes or until crust is lightly browned.

Day 187
Scented Sachet Bags

Materials:
Flowers
Scissors
Shoe box or gift box with a lid
See-through fabric or netting
Needle and thread
Dime-store cologne
Ribbon

Directions: Collect roses or other flowers that smell sweet. Cut away the stems and leaves with scissors. Place the flowers in a shoe box or a gift box and cover. Place the box in a dark, dry place like a closet or an attic. Allow the flowers to dry for ten days. Cut two rectangular shapes out of the fabric which are exactly the same size – the length of each shape should be longer than its width. Thread a needle wit sewing thread, and knot the ends of the thread together. Place the two fabric shapes together. Using a running stitch, sew down one of the long sides a little in form the edge. To make a running stitch, first push the needle through both pieces of fabric near the top of one side and pull the thread until it is stopped by the knot. Now push the needle back through both pieces of fabric a little way from the knot. Continue to pass the needle back and forth through the fabric making small, equally spaced stitches. Now sew along the bottom leaving some extra fabric between your sewing and the bottom edge. Complete the bag by sewing up the other side. The last stitch should be sewn several times. Cut away the extra thread. Cut slits into the extra fabric on the bottom of the bag to make a fringe. Be sure not to cut into the sewn stitches. Sprinkle a little of the cologne on the completely dried flowers. Fill the bag half-full of the dried flowers. Tie the top of the bag with a ribbon and make a bow.

Day 188
Make a Videotape of Your Neighborhood with Your Friends

Day 189

Make Stars and Stripes Sandwiches

Ingredients:
Sandwich Bread
Peanut Butter
Jam
Star-shape cookie cutters

Directions: Make a peanut butter and jelly sandwich by spreading the peanut butter on one slice of bread and the jam on the other. Put them together. Now take the cookie cutter and press down in the center of the sandwich to form a star-shaped sandwich. Make a few sandwiches and repeat with cookie cutter. Then cut some sandwiches lengthwise to form the "stripes" of the sandwiches. Remove crusts.

Day 190

Take a Bubble Bath

Day 191

Walk in the Shoes of Others

Directions: Pretend that you are someone other than yourself. Be an old woman, a baseball player, a tennis player, a hula dancer, a ballerina, a grocery clerk, a teacher, an Easter bunny, a goldfish, a baby, a sumo wrestler, and whatever your mind can think of!

Day 192

Visit a Wildlife Preserve

Day 193

Make a Boomerang

Materials:
Cardboard
Markers
Paint
Scissors

Directions: Cut from the cardboard a boomerang shape. Paint this boomerang.
Let dry. Then use markers to dress it up!

Day 194

Mrs. Potts' Pots of Clay

Materials:
Cornstarch clay (baking soda, cornstarch, water)
Tempera paint in white, black and red

Directions: Make the cornstarch clay by mixing 1 cup baking soda, 1/2 cup
cornstarch, and 2/3 cup water in a saucepan. With the help of a grown-up,
cook the mixture on the stove over medium heat, stirring constantly until it
looks like mashed potatoes. Remove from the stove; let cool. When it is cool
enough to handle, knead the clay on a work surface, adding more cornstarch if
needed to make a soft, pliable clay.
Form a ball of clay and then push your thumbs into the center to create a hole.
Build up the sides of the pot from the hole, stretching it and thinning it so that
the sides are evenly thick. Use a large spoon to press the inside out. Continue
shaping the pot so the top round edge overhangs slightly toward the center. The
pot should have a rounded look. Be sure to flatten the bottom a little so the jar
or pot can rest on its own. Once the pot is shaped, bake it until it is hardened
in a 250° F oven with the help of an adult. Paint the pot white, then paint a
simple bird, flower, or sun design using the black and red colors.

Day 195

Make a Personalized Fortune Cookie Gift

Ingredients:
1/4 cup all-purpose flour
2 tablespoons sugar
1 tablespoon cornstarch
Dash of salt
2 tablespoons cooking oil
1 egg white
1 tablespoon water

Directions: Type your gift recipient's favorite sayings onto a paper. Then cut into small strips. Now make the cookies. In a small mixing bowl, stir together flour, sugar, cornstarch, and salt. Add oil and egg white; stir until smooth. Add water and mix well. With the help of an adult, heat a lightly greased skillet. Pour about a tablespoon of batter into the skillet. Spread batter into a 3 1/2" circle. Cook over low heat 4 minutes or until lightly browned. Flip cookie with wide spatula and cook 1 minute more. Working quickly, place cookie on a pot holder or paper towel. Put a riddle strip in the center (fold paper if necessary). Fold cookie in half; then fold again over the edge of a glass to form a half-moon shape. Let cool. Repeat with remaining batter.

Day 196

Help your Parents Wash Their Car

Day 197

Write a Letter to Yourself

Directions: Write a letter to yourself every year around your birthday. Make it sound like a letter to a dear friend that you love.

Day 198

Magic Hat Trick

Materials:
Hat
Clear plastic up containing grape juice or something to drink

Directions: Ask a friend over to watch you try out this new magic trick. Carefully place the hat over the cup and tell your friend that you are going to drink the contents of the cup without touching the hat. Say some magical words and wave your hands over the hat. Then announce that you have done the trick. Your friend will probably lift up the hat to see what has happened. If not, invite him or her to look under the hat. As your friend lifts the hat, grab the cup and enjoy the drink, showing your friend that you didn't have to touch the hat to drink from the cup.

Day 199

Make Pigs-in-a-Blanket

Ingredients:
Hot dogs
Store-bought crescent rolls
Water

Directions: Unroll the dough from the store-bought crescent rolls, wrap the dough around a hot dog, leaving both ends sticking out. Moisten the dough's edges with water and press together to seal. Put it on a stick and roast over hot coals (camping-style) or bake in a 350°F oven for 15 to 20 minutes.

Day 200

Paint your Toenails or Paint your Mom's Toenails!

Day 201
Window Catchers

Materials:
Sheet of acetate
Pencil
Paper
Tape
Paintbrushes
Paint for glass painting
Scissors

Directions: Draw a circle on a piece of paper. Draw a simple design inside the circle. Tape a sheet of acetate over your drawing. Fill in your design with thin paint and let the paint dry completely. Cut out the acetate circle and tape it onto a window to let sunlight shine through it.

Day 202
Have a Pie-eating Contest

Day 203
Lay on the grass and look up into the clouds

Day 204
Colored Celery Tree

Materials:
Knife
Celery stalk with leaves
2 drinking glasses
Boxed dyes or food coloring (2 colors)
Spoon

Directions: Trim away part of the bottom of the celery. Slice halfway through the center of the celery stalk with a knife. Fill two glasses at least three-quarters full with water. Add a different color of dye or food coloring to the water in each glass. Mix well with a spoon. Add enough dye to make a very strong or dark solution. Place the two glasses next to each other. Slip one end of the cut celery stalk into one glass and the remaining end into the other glass. Let the celery remain in the dye overnight. In the morning, the different dyes will have traveled up the celery stalk and the leaves will have colored beautifully.

Day 205
Have a Water Balloon Toss

Day 206
Visit a Natural History Museum

Day 207
Cinnamon Pull-Apart Bread

Ingredients:
Nonstick cooking spray, 1/2 cup sugar
2 teaspoons ground cinnamon
2 tablespoons butter
2 tablespoons diet margarine
2 pop-cans refrigerated dinner rolls
(can also use the refrigerated French Loaf dough)

Directions: Generously coat a 2-quart casserole dish or 9" x 5" loaf pan with the nonstick cooking spray; set aside. Preheat oven to 375° F. In a small shallow bowl, blend the sugar with the cinnamon. Melt the butter and diet margarine together in a small, microwave-safe shallow bowl using the DEFROST power of your microwave, or melt in a small saucepan and pour into a small shallow bowl. Open the pop-cans and pull the rolls apart and place on a cutting board. Cut each of the rolls in half to make two half-moons using a plastic knife (if you are under 9 years old). Then dip each of the half-moon-shaped pieces of dough into the butter mixture then roll in the sugar mixture to coat all sides. Place the coated pieces of dough on top of each other in the prepared pan. The dough should almost reach the top of the pan or dish. Sprinkle any remaining sugar mixture over the top. Bake in the center of the oven for 18 to 20 minutes, or until the bread is golden brown. Let cool slightly, then remove the bread from the pan and place on a serving dish or plate. Now pull apart the pieces of cinnamon bread with your family or friends!

Day 208
Blow Big Bubbles!

Ingredients:
4 cups water
2 cups liquid dish detergent
2 cups glycerin
2 teaspoons sugar or corn syrup

Directions: Mix the water, detergent, glycerin, and corn syrup in a large basin or dishpan. Take a wire clothes hanger and bend the center of the hanger wider to form a square. Dip in the bubble mixture and wave the hanger around to create big bubbles!

Day 209
Go Bird-Watching

Day 210
Edible Garland

Invite your friends over and create edible garlands that you can string anywhere, any season.

Materials:
1 cup sweetened multigrain cereal or frosted whole-grain oat cereal
2 cups uncooked rigatoni noodles or reduced-fat microwave popcorn
1/2 cup dried cranberries

Creates 1 garland.

Directions: Put all ingredients into their own bowls. Thread a plastic needle (found in craft and sewing stores) with a piece of embroidery thread that is about 4 feet long and tie a big knot at one end. Have everyone thread pieces of popcorn, alternating with cereal and occasionally dried cranberries. When the garland is completed, tie a big knot on the other end and decorate your tree!

Day 211
Aunt Ross' Spiced Apple Cider

Ingredients:
2 quarts (64 ounces) apple cider
10 whole cloves
1 orange cut in half
4 cinnamon sticks

Makes about 8 cups of cider

Directions: Pour the apple cider into a large saucepan and begin to warm over medium heat. Stick the cloves into the orange peel of both halves. Add the orange halves to the apple cider. Now pick four cinnamon sticks from the jar and drop them into the pot of warming cider. After the cider comes to a boil, reduce the heat to a simmer and cook, uncovered, 25 to 35 minutes.

Day 212
Mirror Mirror

Directions: Look at yourself in the mirror and compliment yourself. Say, "I'm a winner," or "I feel great!" or "I am lovable" or "I am special and unique" or "I love to learn" or "I am smart."

Day 213
International Friends

Learn about different cultures through a pen pal who lives in another country.

Day 214
Carnations to Munch On

Materials:
Carrot
Vegetable peeler
Sharp knife
Toothpicks

Directions: Peel the carrot. Cut it into thin slices. Put all the slices in a bowl of cold water and refrigerate overnight. Notice how the slices have curled and become twisted. Spear 3 to 5 slices on a toothpick to make a flower.

Day 215
Say "Hi" to Haiku Poetry

Directions: Write a haiku poem today. Using your imagination, write a 5 syllable, 4 to 5 lines poem. Then read it out loud to someone.

Day 216
Homemade Baby Shampoo

Ingredients:
4 tablespoons dried chamomile blossoms
2 tablespoons dried lavender blossoms
4 drops chamomile essential oil
1 drop rose essential oil
2 tablespoons apple cider vinegar
7 ounces unscented liquid castile soap
Sterilized plastic bottle(s)
Stickers
2 Bowls
Strainer
Deep container
Eyedropper
Whisk
Funnel

Directions: Put dried blossoms into separate bowls. Pour 1/2 cup boiling water over chamomile and 1/4 cup over lavender. Let blossoms stand overnight in warm place. Then strain, pressing on blossoms to extract all liquid. Pour the liquid into deep container. Stir in chamomile and rose essential oils and cider vinegar. Add castile soap. Carefully without creating foam, whisk to blend ingredients thoroughly. Pour shampoo through funnel into clean plastic bottles; seal tightly. Decorate with stickers. Tie a ribbon around the bottle(s) and give as a gift with a sponge or rubber duck.

Day 217

Make "Bug" Juice

Ingredients:
3 kinds of juices: orange juice, apple juice, grape juice, cranberry juice, any kind of juice.

Directions: Mix together to make your own "Bug" juice.

Day 218

Write a letter to a friend you haven't seen in a while.

Daniella

Note from Daniella:
Bonjour! Taste what life has to offer you.
Then cook up something sweet.

Day 219

Go to the Park and People-Watch

Day 220

Time Capsule

Materials:
Box and your things

Directions: Spend one afternoon making a time capsule that captures this particular period in your life. Fill your box with things that remind you of this period in your life. This can be a book, movie tickets, picture of you, piece of jewelry, magazine or anything that you want that you won't miss for a year. Of course, don't put your pet frog in there! Then write a letter to yourself with where you would like to be by next year. Then close the box and label it. Put the box in the back of your closet or somewhere you don't use everyday. Once a year goes by, open this box and see if you are where you wanted to be last year!

Day 221

Learn to Knit

Day 222

Go Bug-Hunting

Day 223

Me Mouse Pad

Materials:
White or light colored craft foam, cut into approximately 8" x 9" pieces
Non-toxic permanent colored markers
Clear vinyl, cut the same size and shape as craft foam
Clear 2" wide book or packing tape, cut to 9" length

Directions: Draw the design of a self-portrait of yourself on one side of the craft foam with the permanent markers. Place a piece of tape approximately 9" long to adhere clear vinyl to craft foam along the top long edge. Then you can slide notes, memos, or photos between the vinyl and the foam. Trim as needed. Add notes and photos under the clear vinyl. You can even put your name on the craft foam to personalize it further.

Day 224
Start a Collecting Club!

Day 225
Do Crossword Puzzles

Day 226
Roses to Munch On

Materials:
Red radishes (1 per rose)
Scallions (1 per rose)
Thin bamboo skewers (1 per rose)
Screws or galvanized nails (2 dozen)
Green cabbage, 1 small head

Directions: The night before -Cut the root end off each radish. Make a series of vertical cuts in each all the way around. Be careful not to cut all the way through. Place the radishes in a bowl of cold water. Refrigerate overnight. The next day, notice how the radishes have "bloomed" or opened up. Cut the root end off each scallion. Insert a skewer in each scallion, pushing it up through one leafy tip (most scallions branch out into two or three leaves). Cut that leaf back just enough to expose the tip of the skewer. Place an opened radish "bloom" on the tip of each scallion "stem." That completes one flower. Slice the cabbage in half. Place it flat-side down inside a bowl. Stick the "Long-stemmed roses" into the cabbage. Shred the remaining half of the cabbage (use a grater or a knife to cut thin slivers). Cover the upturned cabbage base with the shredded cabbage, to look like grass.

Day 227

Double-Chocolate Brownies

Ingredients:

3/4 cup granulated sugar   1/4 cup margarine, softened
1 egg   1/4 teaspoon almond extract
1 1/4 cups all-purpose flour   1/3 cup milk
1/2 teaspoon baking soda   1/2 teaspoon salt
1/2 cup semisweet chocolate pieces 1/4 cup unsweetened cocoa powder
1/4 cup chopped walnuts

Directions: In a mixer bowl cream together sugar and margarine. Beat in egg, milk, and margarine. Stir together flour, baking soda, walnuts, chocolate, cocoa powder, and salt. Add to creamed mixture; mix just till blended. Spread in a greased 9x9x2-inch baking pan. Bake in a 375° oven for 17 to 20 minutes. Remove. Cool cookies and cut into bars. Makes 2 dozen.

Day 228

Have a Bagel Party!

Ingredients:

Peanut Butter Spread
2 tablespoons reduced-fat peanut butter
3 tablespoons low-fat vanilla frosting

Strawberry Spread
1/8 cup reduced-sugar strawberry jam
1/4 cup light cream cheese

Snickerdoodle Spread
1/4 cup light cream cheese
1 tablespoon sugar
1/2 teaspoon ground cinnamon

Directions: Have 3 small serving bowls or custard cups. Add the ingredients under Peanut Butter Spread into one bowl and stir together with a spoon to blend. Add the ingredients under Strawberry Spread together in one bowl and stir together to blend. Add the ingredients under Snickerdoodle Spread into one bowl, then stir together with a spoon to blend. Put a plastic knife or spoon in each of the custard cups with the bagel spreads. Place the spread and bagel pieces in front of everyone. Let everyone serve themselves by spreading the different bagel spreads on the bagel pieces.

Day 229

Book Club

Start a book club with your friends and pick a book to read and discuss every month. Meet at someone's house every month and discuss. Have food ready.

Day 230

Cheetah Lamp Shade

Materials:
Plain white or cream-colored shade
Black cardboard
Scissors
Glue

Directions: Look for a photograph you can copy for the cheetah pattern, and then draw the shapes onto black cardboard. Cut these out and glue them onto a plain white or cream-colored shade.

Day 231

Rain Stick

Materials:
Gift wrap or paper towel tubes
Strips of cardboard
Paper
Tape
Seeds or rice

Directions: Cut out two 4 inch circles out of the paper (trace a cereal bowl for the shape). Put one over the end of the tube, and fold the sides down, and tape around the tube. Cut cardboard strips are narrower than the tube (about 1 inch wide should work). Fold them back and forth like a fan. Put the strips into the tube. The first one should fall to the bottom of the tube. Keep adding strips until they reach the top of the tube.

Pour in 1/4 cup of rice and 2 tbsp of seeds (dried peas, popcorn, or lentils) into the tube.

Tape the other circle over the open end of the tube and tape in place.

Decorate the tube with markers, paints or by gluing on paper or ribbon.

Day 232
Strawberry Jelly

Materials:
1 1/2 pounds of fresh or frozen strawberries
Sieve
Cheesecloth
Sugar
8 small lemon balm leaves
5 sterilized glass jar with tight-fitting lids (1/2-pint)

Directions: Place fresh strawberries in sieve; rinse under cold water. Drain and pat dry. Use thawed frozen berries as it is. Transfer strawberries to the pan. Using a sturdy metal spoon, press berries to extract as much juice as possible. Bring berries to a boil; 2 to 3 minutes. Moisten cheesecloth; wring out. Line sieve with cloth. Pour mixture into lined sieve set over bowl; press with back of spoon. Squeeze to extract all juice; measure. Return the juice to the pan; add an equal amount of sugar. Boil, stirring, 3 minutes. Stir in the lemon balm. Spoon jelly into sterilized jars. Secure lids. Cool upside down.

Day 233
Masquerade Masks Design Get Together

Materials:
Simple store-bought plastic or cloth eye mask
Sequins
Felt or fabric bits
Netting or tulle
Beads
Ribbon
Straws
Feathers

Pom-poms
Glitter
Scissors
White glue or masking tape
Paper clips
Popsicle stick or chopstick

Directions: Invite your friends over for a mask-making party. Have everyone design their masks first. Then lay out all of the decorations so they can see how they fit on the mask. Glue decorations onto the front of the mask from the bottom layer up. For instance, do a base layer of feathers, then glue pom-poms and so on. Make sure everyone glue lots of stuff near the bottom edge of the mask so that it hangs over the lower part of your face. Use paper clips to hold things in place while the glue sets. Let glue dry thoroughly. Add a Popsicle stick or a chopstick to the back side of your mask to add a mask holder. Decorate with ribbons.

Day 234

Bunches of Flowers and Fruits to Munch On

Materials:
Uncolored marzipan (in the gourmet section of your supermarket)
Food colors
Powdered sugar

Directions: Wash your hands. Divide the marzipan into sections, one for each color. Add a few drops of food coloring to each piece of marzipan; leave one section uncolored. Green, yellow, red, and brown are just a few colors that work well for making fruit and flowers. Work the food coloring into the marzipan with your fingers. Make sure the color is evenly distributed. If the marzipan seems sticky, knead in a little powdered sugar to firm it up. Use the marzipan like modeling clay to create flowers and miniature fruit. Roll it between your fingers to make round shapes such as apple, pear, and banana. Use a tiny bit of brown (mix blue, red and yellow to make brown) for stems and the ends of the banana. Flatten some marzipan on your work table (dust the surface with powdered sugar so that the marzipan won't stick to the table). With a small knife cut out shapes such as petals for the flower and leaves.

Day 235

Create a Cool Cap/Hat Rack

Ingredients:
Sandpaper
15" 1x6 pine board
Oil-based or latex paint
Pencil
Drill (Ask an Adult to Use)
(4) 1-inch X 2 1/8-inch Shaker pegs with a built-in wooden "tenon"
White Elmer's glue
(2) 1 1/8-inch screw eyes

Directions: Sand the board's edges. Paint a background color on the rack. Let dry. Lightly mark where the pegs will go: 3 inches apart and 3 inches in from sides. Have an adult drill a 1/2" diameter hole to fit the peg. Sketch a design on the rack; paint carefully. Let dry. Glue the ends of the pegs and tamp them in place. Screw eyes into top for hanging.

Day 236

Make Breakfast for your Parents and Serve them Breakfast in Bed.

Day 237

Rice Krispies Treats

Ingredients:
2 tablespoons margarine or butter
4 cups miniature marshmallows
Food coloring in green or any colors
6 cups Rice Krispies cereal

Directions: Melt the margarine in a large saucepan over low heat. Add the marshmallows and stir until they are completely melted. Remove from the heat. Add 5 drops of your food coloring until the marshmallow mixture turns that color. Add the Rice Krispies cereal and stir until well coated.

Day 238
Go to the Beach and Listen to the Waves

Day 239
Learn Morse Code

Day 240
Learn to Tie a Knot

Day 241
Powerful Words

Directions: Choose a positive word for the week, such as bravery. Read about a character or a person who is believed to have it. Discuss it with friends and family, then practice being brave each day in small ways during the week.

Some words to practice and live:

Able, Awareness, Abundance, Awe, Balance, Beautiful, Bountiful, Brilliant, Bright, Brave, Courageous, Creative, Committed, Challenge, Dedicated, Enthusiastic, Energetic, Excellence, Family, Faith, Friendship, Fortitude, Gentle, Goals, Healing, Humor, Healthy, Integrity, Intuition, Joy, Kindness, Living, Learning, Mentors, Membership, Open-minded, Optimistic, Peaceful, Persistent, Questions, Rest, Relaxation, Self-confidence, Self-esteem, Surprise, Supportive, Strong, Trust, Truthful, United, Vision, Wisdom, Wonder, Zest

Day 242
Table Magic Trick

Materials:
Saltshaker
Paper Napkin
Small coin

Preparation: Put a coin on the table and tell the audience that you are going to push it right through the table. Put the saltshaker on top of the coin, then cover the saltshaker with the napkin "for safety reasons." Place your hands on the napkin on either side of the saltshaker so that you have the saltshaker in your grip. Tell the audience that after a count of three, the coin will go through the table. Now move the saltshaker, covered by the napkin, back and forth from its position on the table to a position just above your lap to see if the coin is gone. Move the saltshaker back and forth three times, checking to see if the coin is still there. Click the saltshaker on the coin each time. On the fourth count, at the point where the saltshaker and napkin are above your lap, gently let the saltshaker drop into your lap and return the napkin, still holding its shape, to its original position above the coin. Release the napkin and, before your audience realizes that the saltshaker is no longer there...bang your hand flat onto the napkin, the coin is still there, but the saltshaker disappeared.

Day 243

Go to an Observatory

Day 244

Fan Pillows

Materials:
(1 pillow) - 1 yard black satin or satin lining fabric; assorted old neckties or similar fabric scraps; 1 yard cording; fiberfill; fusible webbing.

Directions: Cut two 171/4-inch fabric squares. Trim away 7 necktie backs to form single pieces of fabric. But one necktie into a quarter-circle. Using fusible webbing, arrange tie strips into a fan shape with the quarter-circle as the base; iron into place. Cut and piece bias strips of black fabric to cover cording. With fabric's right sides facing, position cording around pillow edge; stitch a 5/8-inch seam, leaving an opening for turning. Turn and stuff with fiberfill; slip-stitch opening.

Day 245

Recycle Your Aluminum Cans and Newspaper

Day 246

Waterlilies to Munch On

Materials:

Orange or grapefruit
Sharp knife (Use With Adult Supervision)
Green paper
Scissors

Directions: Cut a zigzag pattern into the orange or grapefruit with the knife. Be sure to thrust the blade well into the fruit. Work your way around the entire fruit, ending right where you began. Pull the two halves apart. Cut some leaf shapes out of the green paper. Arrange the citrus waterlilies on top of the paper pads.

Day 247

Visit a Petting Zoo

Day 248

Baklava from Greece

Ingredients:

Syrup:

1 cup sugar
1 cup water
11/2 -inch-thick slice lemon

1 stick cinnamon
1 cup honey

Pastry:

4 cups or 1 pound finely ground walnuts
1/2 teaspoon nutmeg
2 cups or 1/2 pound finely ground almonds
2 teaspoons cinnamon
1 1-pound package phyllo pastry, thawed 1/4 cup sugar
11/2 cups or 3 sticks of melted margarine

Directions: Preheat oven to 300°. In a large bowl, combine walnuts, almonds, sugar, cinnamon, and nutmeg. Grease a 9-by-13-inch pan with 2 tablespoons butter. Place 4 sheets of phyllo in the pan, brushing each with melted margarine before adding the next. Butter the fourth sheet also. Sprinkle 1/2 to 3/4 cup of nut mixture over the phyllo. Top nut mixture with 2 more sheets of phyllo, buttering each sheet well. Continue alternating nut mixture with 2 sheets buttered phyllo until both are used up, ending with phyllo. Brush top with butter. With a sharp knife, trim off any excess phyllo on the sides of the pastry.

With a sharp knife, make 11/2-inch-wide lengthwise cuts in the dough. Cut through the top layer only. Do not cut all the way through the dough. Make 11/2-inch diagonal cuts to create diamond-shaped pieces. Again, cut only the top layer. Bake baklava for 1 hour or until golden brown. Remove from oven and place on a cooling rack. Cut through diamonds completely with a sharp knife. Immediately pour the cooled syrup over hot pastry. Cool and serve on dessert plates.

Day 249
Baby-sit your little brother, sister, or neighbor

Day 250
Hangers with Personality

Materials:
Hanger
Cardboard
Small plate
Magazines
Pictures
Craft knife
Rubber mat
Glue

Directions: Lay the hanger on stiff cardboard and trace around it to make the shoulders and neck. Trace a small plate for the head, adding a thickened hook from the top of the hanger. Cut out the whole shape with a craft knife. Remember to cut on a rubber mat.
Use cutouts of facial features from magazines to create a person or cut out pic-

tures of celebrities, animals, whatever you can think of to glue on the head of the hanger.

Day 251

Pick a character from History, and pretend to be that character all day, having people guess who you are.

Day 252

Have a Story-Telling Festival

Directions: Invite your friends over and start off with a character, then each person makes up a story about that character.

Day 253

Pears Helen from France

Ingredients:

1/2 cup chocolate syrup   4 to 8 scoops vanilla ice cream
4 canned pear halves, drained 1/3 cup raspberry or strawberry jam
1 tablespoon hot water

Directions: In the bottom of 4 sherbet glasses or bowls, put 2 tablespoons chocolate syrup. On top of syrup, place 1 or 2 scoops of ice cream. Place 1 pear half, cut side down, on top of each portion of ice cream. Combine jam and water in a separate bowl and spoon mixture over each pear.

Day 254

Watch Pretzels or Cinnamon Rolls are Made at the Mall's Food Court

Day 255
Personalized Switch Plate Cover

Materials:
Contact paper shapes in different patterns
Plastic switch plate cover, including screws for installation
Stickers
Non-toxic permanent marker
Zipper-seal plastic sandwich bag

Directions: Decorate the switch plate cover using the stickers and contact paper shapes. Place the decorated switch plate cover in a plastic zipper-seal sandwich bag, along with the screws or other hardware needed for installing the plate cover.

Day 256
Visit a Chocolate Factory

Day 257
Visit a Nut Farm

Day 258
Pine Cone Candle Holder

Materials:
Yarn
Small, round pine cones
Tin can with label removed (soak off with hot water)
Red poster paint or paper
Paintbrush
Ribbon
Play clay (or any non-hardening clay)
Candle

Directions: Tie two pieces of yarn together around the last ring of petals at the bottom of each pinecone. Be sure each side has a length of yarn hanging from it. Tie two pinecones together by knotting one length of yarn of one pinecone to another length of yarn on a second pinecone. Continue tying pinecones together to form a string of pine cones long enough to fit around the tin can. Paint the in can with red poster paint or cover with red paper. Arrange the cones around the bottom of the can. Tie a ribbon around the can and into a bow. Stick a large ball of play clay onto the bottom of the tin can. Push a candle into the clay.

Day 259
Go Out to a Baseball Game

Day 260
By The Season Natural Necklaces Get Together

Materials:
Silk cord, shoelace, ribbon, string, nylon thread or yarn for stringing
Scissors
Large needles
Hole puncher
Cardboard
White glue

Necklace pieces

Spring: Fresh or dried flowers, ribbons, and lace

Summer: Fake pearls, green leaves or dried seaweed, seashells, starfish

Fall: Autumn leaves, horse chestnut seedpods, nutshells

Winter: Pine needle stems pinecones, cranberries, tiny red bells

Directions: Gather your friends to make some necklaces. Have everyone collect all the things you need to string onto your necklace and lay them out on a table. Arrange them in a line, imagining how they will look when they are on your necklace. Cut the cord or ribbon and tie a big knot from one end of the cord. Thread the needle with the cord and string your objects onto the cord. When you've threaded everything onto your necklace, tie a big knot at the end. Trim the ends.

Day 261

Go to a Basketball Game

Day 262

Invent An Ice Cream Party

Ingredients:
Light vanilla, strawberry, and chocolate ice cream.

Directions: Write invitations asking a small number of your friends or neighbors to come to an "Invent An Ice Cream" party. Tell them you are providing the vanilla, strawberry, and chocolate ice cream as the base ice creams. They need to choose one of those and bring whatever they need to create a new type of ice cream. For example: Inventing a macadamia nut ice cream – they have to bring the macadamia nuts. Set the base ice cream out about 5 minutes before they arrive. Set out medium-size bowls for each of your ice-cream inventors. When your guests arrive, pass out chef hats (from party stores) if you have them. Scoop out about 1 1/2 cups of the base flavor of ice cream each guest needs to make his or her invention. Now they can add their "secret" ingredients to the ice cream in their bowls and stir to combine it. They can next dish out a sample of their new ice cream into plastic cups for everyone to try. Then have a vote on the best ice cream flavor invented!

Day 263

Furry Notebooks

Materials:
Fabric glue
Fabric marker
Fabric scissors
Faux-fur fabric (about 1/2 yard)
Notebook

Directions: Lay fabric wrong side up on work surface. Trace notebook cover onto back side of fabric. Cut out fabric cover. Glue fabric cover onto front of notebook.

Day 264

Visit a Dairy Farm (unless you live on one!)

Day 265

Learn to Whistle

Day 266

Laugh At Yourself

Directions: Learn to laugh at yourself. Make a list of things about you that you think is funny. Then put next to those things a positive phrase. For example: Shortest kid in my class – Can fit in anywhere, can find the best hiding spots.

Day 267

Liquid Art

Materials:
1/3 cup light corn syrup
1/3 cup glycerin (available in drugstores)
1/3 cup water
1/3 cup vegetable oil
4 small glasses
1 tall, clear glass or jar
Food coloring
Funnel

Directions: Pour the corn syrup, glycerin, water, and vegetable oil into four separate cups. Add a few drops of red food coloring to the corn syrup. Add drops of blue to the water. Do not color the oil or glycerin. Pour the red syrup into the glass or jar. Try not to let it dribble down the sides. Use the funnel to pour the glycerin down the inside of the glass. Pour carefully to avoid disturbing the bottom layer. Wash the funnel.
Repeat previous directions - first adding the blue water, then the oil, washing the funnel between steps. The liquids will stay in separate layers if you are careful not to shake the glass.

Day 268

Pineapple Ice

Ingredients:
4 cups 1-inch pineapple pieces
1/2 cup light corn syrup
2 tablespoons lemon juice

Directions: Place all ingredients in blender or food processor. Cover and blend, stopping occasionally to scrape sides, until smooth. Pour into loaf pan, 9x5x3 inches. Cover and freeze about 2 hours or until firm around edges but soft in center. Spoon partially frozen mixture into blender or food processor. Cover and blend until smooth. Pour into pan. Cover and freeze about 2 hours or until firm around edges but soft in center. Spoon partially frozen mixture into blender or food processor. Cover and blend until smooth. Pour into pan. Cover and freeze about 3 hours or until firm. Let stand 10 minutes at room temperature before spooning into dessert dishes. Or you can pour into 1-quart ice-cream freezer. Freeze according to manufacturer's directions.

Day 269

Learn to Play the Harmonica

Day 270

Easy Peach Pie

Ingredients:
1 can of peaches for pie-making
Pre-made piecrust
Whipped topping

Directions: Take piecrust out and thaw (if frozen). Open can of peaches and pour into piecrust. Spread evenly. Fill with whipped topping and spread evenly in fluffy waves.

Day 271
Colorful Height Growth Chart

Materials:
White Cloth window blind
Wooden dowel or broomstick
Tape measure
Fabric paint
Hot Glue
Wood or metal numbers from 1 to 6

Directions: Cut the sides of the blind to fit a small space of wall. Paint a 1"
edge on both sides of the curtain panel. Paint each number a different color.
Now measure the curtain from bottom to top. With the first feet from the bottom, place the number "1" and with the second feet, place the number "2" and
repeat with "3", "4", "5", and "6". Glue the numbers in place. Wait until dry
then hang in place like a curtain against the wall.

Day 272
Take a Nap on a Hammock

Day 273
Toys/Collection Display and Organizer

Materials:
Window Curtain with Tabs
Curtain Rod
Equal Size Square Pieces of Assorted Fabric

Directions: Sew the square pieces of fabric onto the curtain equally spaced
apart. Run curtain rod through curtain tab top and hang up on the wall.

Day 274
Volunteer at your local Art Center

Day 275
Sayings Chart

Materials:
White Cloth window blind
Wooden dowel or broomstick
Fabric paint
Hot Glue
Brush

Directions: Cut the sides of the blind to fit a small space of wall. Paint a 1" edge on both sides of the curtain panel. With brush, paint sayings in different sizes and styles on the blind. Wait until dry then hang in place like a curtain against the wall.

Day 276
Try a new Hairstyle

Day 277
Pet Pillow

Materials:
2 Buttons (Black)
Craft scissors
Embroidery floss in black and white
Embroidery needle
Pink felt (1/2 yard)
Pencil
Polyester filling

Directions: Draw an outline of a large cat's or a rabbit's or a dog's face on a piece of paper. Cut out the pattern. Using a pencil, trace pattern onto fabric two times. Cut out pieces. Sew black buttons onto one piece of fabric with white floss for eyes. Sew pink button below eyes with white floss for nose. Baste-stitch whiskers (for cat), beginning at nose. Stitch pieces together with white floss, leaving 3" opening at bottom of pet. Stuff the pet pillow full, but do not overstuff. Stitch opening closed.

Day 278

Summer Pudding from Italy

Ingredients:
1 10-ounce package frozen unsweetened raspberries, thawed
1 10-ounce package frozen unsweetened sliced strawberries, thawed
1 1-pound package frozen unsweetened blackberries, thawed
1 loaf sliced white bread, several days old
1 cup sugar

Directions: Stir all fruit and sugar together in a large bowl. Let frozen fruit to thoroughly defrost. Meanwhile, cut the crusts off as many bread slices as you will need to line a deep 2-quart bowl. But a round piece for the bottom of the bowl and several overlapping wedges for the sides. Line the bowl with bread and pour in fruit mixture and juices. Cover the top completely with more bread slices. Over the top bread slices, put a plate that is small enough to fit inside the rim of the bowl. Place a heavy weight, such as a brick or a rock, on top to press it down firmly. Refrigerate for at least 24 hours. When ready to serve, remove the weight and plate. To unmold pudding, place a serving plate upside down on top of the bowl. Then, grasping plate and bowl firmly, turn them over quickly. The pudding should slide easily onto the plate. If it doesn't, slide a knife blade around the inside edge of the bowl to loosen it. The fruit juices should now be soaked up by the bread so that the pudding is a rich purple-red color. Serve with a large bowl of fresh whipped cream.

Day 279

Star Quilt

This activity may require adult supervision for younger children.

Materials:
Acrylic felt in pale yellow, 1 1/4 yards, 36" wide
Acrylic felt in orange, 1 yard, 36" wide
Acrylic felt in blue, 12", 36" wide
Thin cardboard for star templates
Two pattern printed (can be stripes or flowers or stars) fabrics, 8" square each
Fusible webbing, 8" x 16"
Thick topstitching thread in pale yellow, orange and blue to match felt
Freezer paper for appliqué stars

Baking parchment paper
Rayon machine thread
Regular sewing thread

Directions: From the pale yellow felt, cut a 34" x 24" rectangle for the backing. Cut a rectangle the same size from the orange felt for the top layer. Trace three star patterns (different sizes) on the cardboard to use as templates. From the orange felt, cut four small stars and four medium stars. From the pale yellow felt, cut eight small stars and eight medium stars. From each of the star fabrics, cut one large star, then iron fusible webbing onto both stars. Baste the two rectangles of felt together and, using matching topstitching thread, stitch two rows around the edges, the first row 1/8 in from the edge and the second 3/8" from the edge. Draw round the large star template onto freezer paper and cut out five stars. Following the quilt plan or in your own arrangement, iron them onto the quilt top, suing baking parchment paper to protect the felt. Stitch around the zipper using the thicker thread to match the bright yellow felt, then remove the paper. Place the two large fabric stars, just slightly offset from the stitching. Iron in place, protecting the surface with baking parchment paper. Satin stitch by machine around the two stars using a rayon thread, or attach by hand with buttonhole stitch. Place the small and medium felt stars at random over the top, trying not to overlap, securing each with a pin. Using regular matching colored sewing thread, stitch down each star with a straight machine stitch around the edges. Using baking parchment paper to protect the surface, press with a cool iron. If you need to wash the quilt, wash gently in warm water and dry flat.

Day 280

Write a News story about Interesting People in your Neighborhood

Day 281

Pretend to Sing Opera

Day 282

Coconut Ice from the Caribbean

Ingredients:
2 cups whole milk
1 cup sugar pinch
3 cups shredded coconut, fresh or packaged
Pinch of cream of tatar

Directions: In a small saucepan, scald milk. Place 2 cups coconut in a sieve. Pour hot milk over coconut while holding sieve over large bowl to catch liquid. Use the back of a spoon to squeeze all of the milk out of the coconut. In a large saucepan, combine coconut milk, sugar, and cream of tartar. Cook over low heat, stirring constantly, until sugar has dissolved. Remove pan from heat and add beaten egg yolk. Beat well with a spoon. Stir in remaining coconut and add 2 or 3 drops almond extract. Taste and add more almond extract if desired. Pour into 2 pie pans. Cover with plastic wrap and place in freezer. Remove coconut ice from freezer after 4 hours and break apart with a fork. Serve immediately.

Day 283

Go to a Hockey Game

Day 284

Phantom Message Trick

Materials:
Paper
Toaster
Lemon juice

Preparation: Write the message, "I am here" in lemon juice on the piece of paper.

Performance: Have everyone sit down while you tell them, "There is a phantom in this room." Then say, "Phantom, are you here?" Take the paper with the lemon juice message over to a toaster and warm the paper slowly until the words, "I am here" appears.

Day 285

Organize your closet, then donate things you don't need or want to charity.

Day 286

Granola-in-a-Bar

Ingredients:

3/4 cup granulated sugar   1/4 cup margarine, softened
1 egg   1/4 cup orange juice
1/4 teaspoon almond extract   1 1/4 cups all-purpose flour
1/2 teaspoon baking soda   1/2 teaspoon salt
1/2 cup granola cereal   1/2 cup raisins
1/2 cup chopped walnuts   1/2 teaspoon ground cinnamon

Directions: In a mixer bowl cream together sugar and margarine. Beat in egg, milk, and margarine. Beat in orange juice and almond extract. Stir together flour, baking soda, walnuts, raisins, cinnamon, and salt. Add to creamed mixture; mix just till blended. Spread in a greased 9x9x2-inch baking pan. Bake in a 375° oven for 17 to 20 minutes. Remove. Cool cookies and cut into bars. Makes 2 dozen.

Day 287

Go to Space Camp

Day 288

Make Tinted Lip Gloss and Eye Shadow

Ingredients:
Petroleum Jelly
Small plastic or tin sealed container
Blush powder

Directions: Fill the container with petroleum jelly. Add some blush powder into the jelly in the container. Mix thoroughly. Now dab on to your lips and eyes for a fresh glossy look!

Day 289

Learn a new Song!

Day 290

Double Chip Tassies

Ingredients:
3/4 cup softened butter (about 1 1/2 sticks)
1 package (3 oz.) cream cheese, softened
1 1/2 cups all-purpose flour
3/4 cup sugar, divided
1 egg, slightly beaten
2 tablespoons butter or margarine, melted
1/4 teaspoon lemon juice
1/4 teaspoon vanilla extract
1 3/4 cups (11 oz.package) Peanut Butter and Milk Chocolate Chips (mixed)
2 teaspoons shortening

Directions: Beat 3/4 cup butter and cream cheese in medium bowl; add flour and 1/4 cup sugar, beating until well blended. Cover, refrigerate about one hour or until dough is firm. Shape dough into 1-inch balls; press each ball onto bottom and up sides of about 36 small muffin cups (1 3/4" in diameter.) Heat oven to 350°F. Combine egg, remaining 1/2 cup sugar, melted butter, lemon juice and vanilla in small bowl; stir until smooth. Set aside 1/3 cup chips; add remainder to egg mixture. Evenly fill muffin cups with chip mixture. Bake 20 to 25 minutes or until filling is set and lightly browned. Cool completely; remove from pan to wire rack. Combine reserved 1/3 cup chips and shortening in small microwave-safe bowl. Microwave at HIGH (100%) 30 seconds; stir. If necessary, microwave additional 15 seconds at a time, stirring after each heating, until chips are melted and mixture is smooth when stirred. Drizzle over tops of tassies. Makes about 3 dozen cookies.

Day 291

Finance Class with Parents

Take a class with your parents on finances. You'll learn about savings, bank accounts, interests, loans, and more.

Note from Rose:
Performers know Practice Makes Perfect.
Perform with Passion!

Day 292

Natural Colorful Crystals

Materials:
Powdered alum, available in the spice section of the supermarket
Water
A small pan
A wooden spoon
Food coloring (for amounts, see below)
Several small jars
Paper towels

Directions: Measure 4 teaspoons of water and 3 teaspoons of alum into the pan.
Add drops of food coloring to achieve the desired color
Bring the mixture to a complete boil, stirring for a few seconds until all of the alum is dissolved.

Allow the mixture to cool two minutes. Carefully pour the alum solution into the jar, and let it sit uncovered and undisturbed for three days. Soon you will begin to see crystals forming at the bottom of the jar. Do not move the jar. After three days, carefully pour off the excess water and gently remove the crystals. Spread them evenly on a paper towel to dry.

Day 293

Take a CPR and First Aid Class from your local American Red Cross Center or Community College.

Day 294

Caribbean Bananas

Ingredients:
4 medium bananas
2 tablespoons melted margarine
1 tablespoon lemon juice
1/2 teaspoon ground allspice
1/3 cup packed brown sugar

Directions: Heat oven to 350°. Cut bananas crosswise into halves; cut each half lengthwise into halves. Place cut sides up in square baking dish, 9x9x2 inches. Mix margarine, lemon juice and allspice; brush over bananas. Sprinkle with brown sugar. Bake uncovered about 15 minutes or until bananas are hot.

Day 295

Go to the Museum

Day 296

Creative Clipboard

Materials:
Thick cardboard, cut into 9" x 12" pieces
Paint, thinned slightly with water
Paintbrushes
Metal bulldog clip
Non-toxic permanent markers

Directions: Paint the cardboard lightly, but don't apply too much paint so the surface is smooth. After the surface is dry, write messages to the recipient on top of the painted area using non-toxic permanent markers (For example: "Grandma's Grand Ideas.) Attach the bulldog clip to the top of the finished clipboard. Attach a few sheets of paper wit the clip to create a useful gift for anyone.

Day 297

Clean out Your Closet

Day 298

Take a Baby-sitting Class

Day 299

Peanut Butter Slices

Ingredients:

1 egg
1/2 cup margarine
2 teaspoons vanilla
1/2 teaspoon salt
1/2 cup creamy peanut butter

3/4 cup granulated sugar
1 3/4 cups all-purpose flour
1/2 teaspoon baking powder
3 tablespoons milk

Directions: In a mixer bowl cream together sugar, peanut butter, margarine. Blend in egg, vanilla and milk. Stir into creamed mixture till blended. On clear plastic wrap, shape dough into two 6-inch-long rolls. Wrap and chill thoroughly. Remove one roll from refrigerator. Unwrap. Reshape slightly to round flattened side. Carefully cut into thin (about 1/8-inch) slices. Place on a greased baking sheet. Bake in a 375° oven for 8 to 10 minutes or till lightly browned. Remove from baking sheet to a wire rack. Repeat with remaining roll. Makes 4 dozen cookies.

Day 300

Noah's Ark

Directions: Use numbered slips of paper, two of each kind, and write the name of an animal or bird that can be imitated. Have a duplicate number list of all slips given out. Select a few players to represent Noah's family. Give out one set of slips to the boys and another to the girls. Players find the persons with matching names for partners. Each couple is given a number. Noah's family stands in one corner, and Noah calls a number. The couple having that number comes to the corner where Noah's family is. Before being admitted to the ark they must imitate the sound or pantomime the animal named on their slips. As soon as the animal is recognized by any of Noah's family, the couple is admitted to the ark. The variety of animals and birds possible is as broad as the universe: ducks, pigs, sheep, owls, bears, frogs, lions, etc.

Day 301

Collect Can Food and Start a Food Drive in your Neighborhood

Day 302

Make Multi-Colored Lemonade

Ingredients:
Lemons
Lemon or Orange Juicer
Water
Sugar
Ice
Food Coloring
2 or 3 pitchers

Directions: Make lemonade by cutting the lemons in halves and squeezing it into one pitcher. Add water, ice, sugar. Then mix. Evenly distribute the lemonade into the other pitchers. In each pitcher, add a food color. Add a few drops of red to make pink lemonade in one pitcher. Add a few drops of green to make green lemonade. Add a few drops of blue to make blue lemonade.

Day 303

Make Your "Signature" Chicken Soup

Ingredients:
2 cups chicken broth
Alphabet pasta

Directions: Have an adult help heat up the chicken broth in a pan on a stove. In the meantime, sort through the pasta to pick out the initials of your first and last names. Pick out as many of the letters as you can find. When the broth begins to boil, pour in the letters of your "Signature" and stir until pasta is soft. Turn off the stove and serve in a bowl with crackers.

Day 304

Visit an Aquarium

Day 305

Milk Pudding from Brazil

Ingredients:

4 eggs   1/3 cup sugar
1 tablespoon water   1/2 cup whole milk
1 14-ounce can sweetened
   condensed milk

Directions: With a hand mixer or in a blender, beat eggs. Add condensed and whole milk and blend well. Set custard mixture aside. Heat sugar and water over medium-high heat in a small saucepan, stirring constantly, until sugar caramelizes or turns brown and syrupy. Quickly pour sugar mixture into bottom of oven-proof mold or bowl, coating the bottom and sides of container. Pour custard mixture into the mold. Bake at 350° for 45 minutes, or until a toothpick inserted I the center comes out clean. Chill until ready to serve. Turn onto platter. The pudding will be covered with a caramel sauce.

Day 306

Nicknames

Directions: With your group of friends or family, come up with cute or neat nicknames for each other. Then vote on which nicknames are the best!

Day 307

Zebra Pillow

Materials:

White Fabric cut into two 14" x 14" pieces
Pins
Scissors
Thread
Black felt

Directions: Pin the two fabric pieces together. Starting about half an inch from the edge, sew the two pieces together. Leave a 10" space on one edge to allow room fro the pillow. Trim off the corners, then turn the case inside out. Push in pillow stuffing and neatly sew up the open edge. Cut out strips from the felt and glue them straight onto the pillow cover to resemble a zebra strip pattern.

Day 308

Go to a Movie Matinee

Day 309

Garage Sale

Directions: Help your family get rid of things they no longer need. Have every-one pitch in for a Garage Sale. Gather anything your family would like to sell, then set a date for a garage sale. With the help of your parent, create a catchy and fun flyer announcing your garage sale and pass this around to people in your neighborhood. On the day of your garage sale, place everything out on your lawn. Have your family work different shift or all at once to answer cus-tomer questions and make sales. Have fun!

Day 310

Biscuit Tortoni from Italy

Ingredients:
3/4 cup chilled whipping cream
1/2 cup almond macaroon cookie crumbs
1 teaspoon almond extract
3 tablespoons sugar
2 tablespoons chopped maraschino cherries
1/4 cup chopped toasted almonds

Directions: Line 6 muffin or custard cups with paper cupcake liners. Beat whip-ping cream and sugar in a chilled bowl until stiff. Set aside 2 tablespoons maca-roon crumbs. Fold rest of crumbs, almond extract, cherries, and almonds into whipped cream. Spoon mixture into prepared cups and sprinkle with remaining crumbs. Cover with plastic wrap and freeze until firm.

Day 311
Water Music

Materials:
8 glasses
Water
Teaspoons

Directions: Line up eight glasses of about the same size and shape. Fill the first glass about 1/8th full of water for the high note, the second glass should be 1/4 full, the third glass should be 3/8ths full for the next note, and so on. Each glass should sound like a note on the scale. You may need to tune your scale (add or remove water with teaspoon) until each note rings true. Use a metal teaspoon to gently tap out the scale and any other melodies you know

Day 312
Plant a Bonsai Tree

Materials:
A juniper tree
Soil
Small Plant Container
Pebbles
Pruning Shears

Directions: Trim the juniper tree to fit into the plant container. Place in the plant container and cover roots with soil. Add pebbles to cover the top of the soil. Water by soaking entire container with tree in water.

Day 313
Bath Mitt Puppets

Materials:
Old washcloths or face clothes in different colors
Chalk
Scissors
Needles, thread, straight pins

Felt in different colors
Buttons (for eyes)
Pom-poms
A pink sponge
Yarn
Ribbon and trim

Directions: Place your hand on the center of a washcloth, sticking out your thumb and pinky finger on either side. Trace around your hand with chalk, but leave extra room around your hand to sew the seam. Cut the pattern out, trace it onto another washcloth, then cut that out, too. Sew facial details onto the front of your puppet. Place right sides of the puppet body together and pin the pieces together. Sew along the edge of the puppet body, leaving the bottom edge open for your hand. Turn the body right side out. Smooth flat.

Day 314
Microwave Science Experiment

In this experiment, see which foods heat faster – those with lots of water or those with little water

Materials: Microwave oven
Food with lots of water
Food with little water

Directions: Heat both foods together and see which heats faster – the food with more water or the food with little water.

Day 315
Read to the Elderly at a nearby Retirement Home

Day 316
Visit New Neighbors

Day 317
Baked Maple Apples

Ingredients:
4 medium cooking apples
2 teaspoons margarine
1/4 cup reduced-calorie maple-flavored syrup

Directions: Heat over to 375°, core apples; peel 1" strip of skin from around the middle of each apple, or peel upper half of each apple to prevent splitting. Place apples upright in ungreased square baking dish, 8x8x2 inches. Place 1/2 teaspoon margarine and 1 tablespoon maple-flavored syrup in center of each apple. Pour water into baking dish until 1/4 inch deep. Bake uncovered 30 to 40 minutes or until apples are tender when pierced with fork. Spoon syrup in dish over apples several times during baking.

Day 318
Attend a Dance Performance

Day 319
Bend Water

Materials:
A hard rubber or plastic comb, or a balloon
A sink and water faucet.

Directions: Turn on the faucet so that the water runs out in a small, steady stream, about 1/8 inch thick.

Charge the comb by running it through long, dry hair several times or rub it vigorously on a sweater.

Slowly bring the comb near the water and watch the water "bend."
This project can also be done with a balloon.

Day 320

Almond Meringues with Fresh Fruit from Chile

Ingredients:

3 egg whites at room temperature   3/4 teaspoon vanilla
1/4 teaspoon cream of tartar   3/4 cup sugar
3/4 cup freshly chopped toasted almonds   Pinch of salt
3/4 cup sliced fresh fruit or berries

Directions: Preheat the oven to 300°. Cover a baking sheet with kitchen parchment paper or heavy-duty aluminum foil with dull side up. Beat egg whites, cream of tartar, vanilla, and salt until stiff peaks form. Add the sugar, 1 tablespoon at a time, and beat well after each addition. Continue beating until the mixture, called a meringue, is stiff and glossy. Gently fold in the almonds. With a spoon, from 6 evenly divided mounds of meringue, about 11/2 inch apart, on the lined baking sheet. Using the back of the spoon, build up the sides and make a small hollow in the center of each mound to form a netlike shape.

Bake at 300° for 20 to 25 minutes. Turn the oven off. Let the meringues cool in the oven. When cool, remove the foil or parchment paper from the meringues. When ready to serve, clean, peel, and slice the fruit. Place the meringues on individual plates and top them with fruit.

Day 321

Homemade Certificates for a Special Recipient

Materials:

Unlined index cards – 4" x 6" cut in half length-wise
Markers
Library pocket
Magnetic tape
Glue
Sequins

Directions: Think about or find out what kind of things you and the recipient can do together (for example: go to the library, read a book, go for a walk, help cook dinner, wash the car, go out for ice cream, go to a movie.)

Write five or six selected activities on the index cards reflecting the activities to be done together. Use markers to decorate the blank side of each coupon. Decorate the library pocket using the glue and sequins. Place a piece of magnetic tape on the back of the pocket and place the coupons inside.

Day 322

Pretend You're at A Spa with Friends

Directions: Put a facial mask on and paint your nails. Put moisturizer on your skin.

Day 323

Dream a Dream!

Materials:
Slips of paper and pen or pencil and cup.

Directions: In a group, each person writes on a slip of paper what he or she wants to be doing in ten years. Then everyone puts the paper into a cup. Everyone pulls out a paper and one by one, read this aloud. Together everyone guesses whose future it is.

Day 324

Sunshine, Flower, or Sports Photo or Memo Holder

Materials:
Self-hardening clay, plain or colored
Metal spatula
Photo of the gift recipient
Thin paintbrush
Tempera Paint

Directions: Work a small, ball-size piece of clay into a solid, freestanding shape. Use multiple colors to add designs and features to the creation (sun, flower, or baseball or some sports objects for example). Leave a space on the top for a slit for the photo. Cut a slit in the top of the holder approximately one to two inches in length and deep enough to hold a photo upright. After the clay dries, paint the clay holder, using a paintbrush and tempera paint. Let paint dry, then slide the photo into the slit to complete the personal gift.

Day 325
Paint Your Lampshade

Day 326
Movie Critic

Directions: Rent a movie and invite your friends over. Afterwards, discuss the movie like movie critics and give the movie your own form of ratings. For examples: 4 out of 5 Starfish.

Day 327
Take Violin Lessons

Day 328
Mini Tornado in a Bottle

Materials:
Two empty one-liter soft drink bottles, rinsed out and with labels removed.
Rubber or steel washer that has a small hole and is the same width as the tops of the bottles
Roll of strong electrical, or duct, tape
Water

Directions: Tape the washer to the top of either bottle, as shown. (Make sure the tape doesn't cover the hole in the washer.)
Fill that bottle three-fourths full of water.

Place the empty bottle upside down on top of the washer. Tape the bottles securely together.

Turn the bottles over so the one on top holds the water. Quickly swirl the bottles in a big circle several times and place the bottom bottle on a flat surface. When you stop, the water should start swirling down in a tornado-shaped funnel.

Day 329

Travel Journal

Materials:
Notebook
Postcards
Glue

Directions: Take all your postcards and overlap them together. Photocopy this, then use the copy to cover the front and back of your notebook. Glue underneath.

Day 330

Mango with Cinnamon from Mexico

Ingredients:
1 1-pound can mangoes
1/4 cup shredded coconut
1 teaspoon cinnamon

Directions: Chill can of mangoes overnight in the refrigerator. To serve, place each mango section in a dessert dish or fruit cup, top with coconut, and sprinkle lightly with cinnamon.

Day 331

Special Door Hanger

Materials:
White poster board, cut into a 4" x 12" rectangle
Crayons
Photo or child, trimmed
Glue
Permanent marker
Clear contact paper

Directions: Cut a three-inch circle near one end of the poster board for the doorknob. This should resemble a hotel room door hanger. Make sure this hole fits around a standard-size doorknob.

Decorate the door hanger with crayons. Glue the photo to the door hanger. Use the permanent marker to write your name and the date on the back of the hanger. A special message may be added to the front of the door hanger. Cover the door hanger with clear contact paper, trimming away the contact paper from the hole near the top.

Day 332
Plant a Victory Garden in Your Yard

Materials:
Vegetable Seeds
(Tomato, Snow Peas, Cabbage, Carrot, and Other Vegetables)
Shovel

Directions: Clear a spot in your yard or backyard (with your parent's permission) and lay out the seeds, according to the directions on the seed packet, in the ground. Finish and water.

Country Vegetable Basket

Materials: 10 snow peas
3 large potatoes
2 leeks
1 artichoke
2 ears of corn
2 onions
4 tomatoes
Basket with handles
Brown wrapping paper (2 sheets)
Raffia or cooking string
Sunflower with leaves
Large Ribbon (Burlap or Sunflower-print or Gingham-print for the country look)

Directions: Remove all dirt and limp leaves from fresh vegetables. Crumple paper and place in the bottom of the basket. Remove the leaves from the Sunflower and drape them over the basket rim. Carefully peel back the husks from the corn, but do not remove. Discard the silk. Trim the snow peas. Tie 5 of them together with cooking string or raffia. Arrange potatoes, ears of corn, artichoke, leeks, tomatoes, and onions decoratively in the basket. Arrange the sunflower and bunches of snow peas among the other vegetables in the basket. Tie the ribbon around the basket handle with a note to the gift recipient.

Day 333
Have a Snowball Fight

Day 334
Hot Apple Cider

Ingredients:
Apple Cider or apple juice
Cinnamon Stick

Directions: Any day is a great day for hot apple cider. Pour apple cider or apple juice into a microwave proof mug and heat in microwave for 30 minutes until hot. Take out of microwave and put in cinnamon stick.

Day 335
Create a Comic Book

Materials:
Notebook
Markers

Directions: Invite some friends over. Then brainstorm on a story that you can draw. Draw each scene with your markers to create a story. Afterwards, share the story with other friends and family.

Day 336
Take tap dancing lessons

Day 337

Edible Snowball

Materials:
Less than 3 cups low-fat vanilla frozen yogurt or ice milk
About 1/3 cup low-fat milk
1/2 cup flaked coconut
4 birthday candle holders and candles

Makes 4 snowballs

Directions: Make a perfect ice-cream scoop using an ice-cream scooper. Freeze the scoops in individual dishes for 30 minutes. When the ice-cream scoops are hard, everyone can pick them up and roll them first into the low-fat milk and then in a shallow dish (such as a pie pan) filled with the flaked coconut.

Day 338

Celebrations Family Book

Materials:
Notebook or Journal

Directions: Celebrate the little things as well as the big things in life. Leave this book in an area like the kitchen for everyone in the family to write in and read.

Day 339

Game of Who Am I?

Can be played with 3 or more Players

All the players except one in this game know the secret identity. One player leaves the area or covers his ears while the rest of the group agrees on a well-known person who may be real or fictional and recognizable by everyone participating. The player then returns to the group and asks everyone, "Who am I?" Each of the other players in turn makes a statement giving a clue to the mystery person's identity. For example, if the person is Superman, one clue might be, "You are not from Earth." Another is "You are a man." The clues should be accurate and informative enough to give the guesser a chance at figuring out who the person is. But not so obvious. After each player has given one clue, the guesser has three chances to name the correct person. If the guesser is stumped, the other players claim victory. Each player should get a chance to be the guesser.

Day 340

Friends and Family Foam Magnets

Can be a group activity with 2 or more people

Materials:
Craft foam, various colors, cut into a variety of people shapes
Craft foam shapes
Wiggly eyes or small buttons
Non-toxic permanent markers
Scissors
Glue
Yarn, cut into small pieces
Ribbon, lace, or fabric scraps
Magnetic tape, cut into pieces

Directions: Choose several craft foam people. Add facial features using wiggly eyes or small buttons and non-toxic permanent markers. Cut craft foam pieces into triangles, rectangles, and squares to create clothes with these shapes. Glue to craft foam people. Use yarn pieces and other scraps to create hair or decoration for clothing. Allow foam people to dry. Attach magnetic tape to the back of each figure. Magnets hold memos, photos, or artwork.

Variation: Instead of attaching a magnet to the back of each figure, attach bar pins to make foam people pins.

Day 341
Birdbath

Materials:
2-liter clear plastic bottle, cut off approximately 5" from top
1-liter clear plastic bottle, cut off approximately 3" from bottom
Scissors or utility knife (use with adult supervision)
Non-toxic oil pastels

Plastic bottle lids
Materials to put in base like plastic beads, sequins, decorative marbles, pebbles, or shells
Glue gun and glue sticks (use with adult supervision)

Directions: Have an adult cut off the neck portion of one of the 2-liter clear plastic bottles that has already been cut off five inches from the top. Decorate the outside of the cut portion with non-toxic oil pastels. Add lots of color. Push the decorated piece into another cut top from a 2-liter plastic bottle) with neck remaining). This will protect the oil pastel decoration. Screw a plastic lid to the decorated funnel shape. Set aside. Place a variety of materials into the base of the cut-off bottom portion of the 1-liter bottle. This will serve as the birdbath stand. Fill it about half full, allowing room for the birdbath top. Push the decorated top with lid side down into the base containing decorative materials. Some may have to be moved slightly so that the top sets securely. Use a hot glue gun with adult supervision to fasten the pieces together. The birdbath is ready to fill with water.

Day 342

Make a Sandcastle at the Beach or Anywhere with Sandbox Sand

Day 343

Fun Pillowcase

Materials:
Fleece fabric (1 yard)
Fabric scissors
Feather boa
Sewing needle
Tape measure
Thread that matches the fabric

Directions: Fold the fabric in half widthwise and baste-stitch sides about 3/4" seams. Baste-stitch boa to the top of the pillowcase opening.

Day 344

Easy Almond-Lemon Sticky Buns

Buy frozen bread dough from store. Thaw. Let rise one; punch down. In a small saucepan, combine 1/2 cup sugar, 1/3 cup dark corn syrup, 4 tablespoons margarine, 1 teaspoon finely shredded lemon peel, and 2 tablespoons lemon juice. Cook and stir just till sugar dissolves and mixture boils. Pour in the bottom of an ungreased 13x9x2-inch baking pan. Sprinkle 3/4 cup toasted sliced almonds over. On a lightly floured surface, roll dough into a 16x8-inch rectangle. Brush with 2 tablespoons melted butter. Combine 1/4 teaspoon ground nutmeg, sprinkle over dough. Beginning with a long side, roll up jelly roll style; seal edge. Cut into sixteen 1-inch slices. Place, cut side down, atop sugar mixture in pan. Cover and let rise in a warm place till nearly double, 30 to 45 minutes. Bake in a 375° oven for 20 to 25 minutes. Immediately loosen sides and turn out onto a wire rack placed atop waxed paper to catch drippings. Makes 16 rolls.

Day 345

Corkboard

Materials:
Paint
Shallow dishes
Thin sheets of cork, cut in 5" x 7" pieces or larger
2 pieces of thick cardboard, cut to size of cork
Sponge shapes
Collage materials such as buttons, colored foam shapes, and stickers
Yarn, cut to 8" or larger piece
Glue

Directions: Put a small amount of paint in each shallow dish. Decorate the sheet of cork by making sponge prints on one side. After the paint dries, glue collage materials on the cork to form a border around the edge. Allow glue to dry. Glue two pieces of equal-sized cardboard on top of each other to double the thickness. Construct a hanger by poking two holes close to one edge of the cardboard pieces and stringing with yarn. Glue the decorated cork sheet on top of cardboard pieces. Allow to dry.

Day 346

Family Tree T-Shirts

Materials:
Cotton T-shirts for everyone in your family.
Paint glue (Black, Yellow, Brown, Red, Blue)
Cardboard to fit under t-shirt
Colorful ribbons

Directions: Put the cardboard in the t-shirt until the shirt is flat and stretched out. Paint a stick figure of everyone in your family including pets. Draw a tree with green leaves in the background. Write their names on the bottom of each figure. Repeat with each t-shirt until done. Let the glue dry. Then fold t-shirts and roll up. Then tie a ribbon around the roll. Present each t-shirt to each family member as a gift.

Day 347

Cookie Jar Gifts (Oatmeal Bars)

Materials:
Quart glass jar
Flour, 1/4" cup
Baking soda, 1/4 teaspoon
Salt, 1/4 cup
Quick oats, 4 cups
Brown sugar, 1 cup
Chopped nuts or candy (covered chocolate pieces), 1/4 cup
Measuring spoons and cups
Wide-mouth funnel (optional)
Bowl
Spoons

Directions: Wash hands with soap and water. Measure and mix together flour, baking soda, and salt in a bowl. Pour half of this mixture into jar and pack down with spoon.
Measure and pour in half of oats required. Pack down with spoon. Measure and pour in half of brown sugar. Pack down with spoon.
Measure and pour in all of chopped nuts or chocolate pieces. Pour in remaining ingredients in order, flour mix, oats, and brown sugar. Reminder: pack down between each added ingredient. Put on the decorated lid. Attach the

recipe for Oatmeal Bars found on the following day below and invite the recipient of your cookie jar gift to come over the next day to make the Oatmeal Bars.

Day 348

Oatmeal Bars

Ingredients:
Dry mix from quart jar
1/4 cup butter or margarine
1/4 cup white or dark corn syrup
1 teaspoon vanilla
Glass mixing bowls
Mixing spoon

Directions: Pour dry mix from jar into bowl and stir. Put butter or margarine, syrup, and vanilla into another glass mixing bowl. Melt in a microwave by cooking for 15- 20 seconds and stirring until liquid. This can also be done on the stovetop in a cooking pan. Remove from the microwave and add dry ingredients. Mix thoroughly. Press dough into the bottom of 9" x 13" pan. Bake at 350° for about 10 minutes or until lightly browned. Remove from oven and with metal spatula cut into desired shape. Let cool before removing from pan. Share with each other and a glass of milk.

Day 349

Just-Right Jeans

Materials:
Jeans or Denim Shorts
Ribbons
Rhinestone or Buttons
Fabric glue

Directions: Position and generously glue ribbons onto jeans. Fold over ribbon ends and overlap on inside of jean leg on seam. Position and glue buttons and Rhinestones onto ribbons and jeans as desired. Let dry overnight.

Day 350

Plant a Tree in Your Yard

Day 351

Truffles

Ingredients:
2/3 cup whipping cream
2 cups (12-oz. Package) of semi-sweet chocolate chips
2 teaspoons vanilla extract

Directions: Heat cream in heavy, 2-quart saucepan just to boiling. Remove from heat. Add chocolate chips; stir with whisk until melted and smooth. Stir in vanilla. Pour into medium bowl. Cover, refrigerate about 3 hours or until firm. Line baking sheet with wax paper. Drop chocolate mixture by heaping teaspoons onto prepared baking sheet. Freeze about 45 minutes or until firm. Place desired coatings in separate bowls. Shape frozen chocolate truffles between hands to form 1-inch balls. Roll in desired coatings. Cover and refrigerate about 2 hours. Serve cold. Truffles keep in an airtight container in refrigerator for 1 week. Makes 30 truffles.

Day 352

Go Window Shopping with a Favorite Aunt

Day 353

Make Fun Slime

Materials:
Cornstarch
Water
Food coloring

Directions: Mix 1 cup of cornstarch with 1 cup of water. Use your hands to mix it until it is a smooth texture. You can change the texture by adding a 2nd cup of cornstarch. Kids love adding food color or paint to make the slime. They have fun making it resemble different icky substances and their imagination is more vivid then most parents want to hear described in detail! Store in a covered container. It will keep for several days.

Day 354

Create Your Own Rainbow

Materials:
Wide-mouthed, smooth, circular glass jar or large plain drinking glass filled with water
Small mirror
Flashlight

Directions: Place the mirror inside the water-filled jar. Tilt the mirror slightly upward. In a very dark room with white walls, shine the flashlight onto the mirror. A rainbow will appear.

Day 355

Scented Door Freshener

Materials:
Nature items, such as flowers, shells, nuts, pine needles, leaves
Hole punch
Zipper-seal plastic sandwich bag
Cinnamon stick
Colorful collage materials
Ribbon

Directions: Go for a nature walk to collect small nature items. Look at what you've collected on the walk and select the items to use for a door freshener. Make two holes in the sandwich bag, one in each of the top corners, just under the zipper seal, using the hole punch. Put the nature items, collage materials, and the cinnamon stick in the plastic bag. Thread the ribbon through the holes in the bag, creating a handle large enough to hang on a doorknob. Seal the sandwich bag. Hang the freshener on your bedroom doorknob or in the bathroom.

Day 356

Easy Soft Pretzels

Buy frozen bread dough from store. Thaw. On a lightly floured surface, roll dough into a 15x12-inch rectangle. Cut into strips 15 inches long and 1/2 inch wide. Roll each strip into a rope 20 inches long. Twist into a pretzel shape.

Let rise, uncovered, in a warm place 30 minutes. In a large kettle dissolve 3 tablespoons salt in 2 quarts boiling water. With a slotted spoon, lower 1 or 2 pretzels at a time into the boiling water; boil 1 to 2 minutes. Remove to paper toweling with a slotted spoon. Pat dry. Arrange 1/2 inch apart on a well-greased baking sheet. Combine 1 slightly beaten egg white and 1 tablespoon water; brush atop pretzels. Sprinkle lightly with a little coarse salt, if desired. Bake in a 400° F oven for 20 minutes or till golden. Cool on a wire rack. Makes 24.

Day 357
Host a Pretzel Party!

Ingredients:
1 11-ounce pop-can of refrigerated breadstick dough or French loaf dough
Nonstick cooking spray
Vinegar
Pretzel salt

Dips for Pretzels
Pizza sauce
Salsa
Cinnamon glaze (make a glaze with 1 cup confectioners powdered sugar, 1/4 teaspoon ground cinnamon, 1/2 teaspoon vanilla extract, and 1 tablespoon water)

Directions: Pop open the breadstick dough cans. Separate the dough into individual breadsticks, following the perforations. Preheat oven to 350°F. Shape the dough into a pretzel by making the half point in the breadstick dough the bottom point of a heart shape. Then bring both ends up and around to shape the top curves of a heart. Twist the two ends around each other once then press the ends to each side of the bottom portion of the heart. Place the pretzels on a cookie sheet coated with nonstick cooking spray or lightly greased. Brush the top of each pretzel with vinegar (using a child's paintbrush or pastry brush), and then sprinkle a pinch of pretzel salt over the top of each pretzel. Bake until lightly browned, about 15 minutes. Pour assorted dips in small bowls and arrange on the table and let everyone proceed with their pretzel party.

Day 358

Person of the Year!

Materials:

Paper and pen or pencil.

Directions: Sit down with your parent or grandparent in a comfortable place and pretend that you are writing an article for the Times, Fortune, or other large world-read magazine. Ask as many of these questions to this person of the year as mood will allow:

What is your favorite dessert? Movie or TV show?

If you could go anywhere in the world, where would it be?

What makes you happy?

What makes you sad?

Which animal are you most like?

Do you have a hero or heroine that you admire?

Which is your least favorite household chore?

Who do people say you look most like?

Then write this down. Continue this next day.

Day 359

Person of the Year Collage

Materials:

Magazines, poster board, scissors, glue, and markers.

Directions: From the information you gathered yesterday during your interview with the person of the year, find pictures from the magazines that seem similar to some of the words that best describes the person of the year. For example: Favorite dessert is a cake. Find pictures of a cake or something like that. Cut out the pictures and glue them on the poster board. Write the word, "Cake" or whatever is their favorite dessert somewhere on the poster board. Do the same for each question. Soon you will have a collage of pictures and words that describes this person of the year. After you are done, present this to this special person!

Day 360
Personal Chip Clips

Materials:
Cardboard cut into a 2" x 3" rectangle
Small stickers
Markers
Clothespin
Glue
Non-toxic permanent marker

Directions: Decorate the cardboard rectangle with stickers and markers. Glue the decorated rectangle to one side of a clothespin. After the glue dries, use the permanent marker to personalize the Chip Clip with the recipient's name. For example, "Mom's Chip Clip" can be written directly on the side of the clothespin or in a blank space on the decorated cardboard.

Day 361
Wreath-Decorating Party

For Groups of 2 and Above

Materials:
Fresh or silk green wreath
Flowers, shells, candy canes, ribbons, pinecones, decorative balls, colorful popcorn, personal trinkets (small dolls, stuffed animals, postcards, miniature picture frames)
Craft wire or florist tape

Directions: At a large table, arrange your decorative items. Each person gets a wreath to decorate with the items on the table. When finished, people can take home their wreath.

Day 362

Carmel-Pecan Chews

Ingredients:
3/4 cup granulated sugar
1/4 cup margarine, softened
1 egg
2 tablespoons milk
1 teaspoon vanilla
1 1/4 cups all-purpose flour
1/2 teaspoon baking soda
1/2 teaspoon salt
1/4 cup chopped pecans
1/4 teapoon ground nutmeg

Caramel Topping:
1/4 cup packed brown sugar
2 tablespoons margarine
2 tablespoons water
1 teaspoon vanilla
3/4 cup shifted powdered sugar
1/4 cup chopped pecans
1/4 cup flaked coconut

Directions: In a mixer bowl cream together sugar and margarine. Beat in egg, milk, and margarine. Beat in egg, milk, and vanilla. Stir together flour, baking soda, pecans, ground nutmeg, and salt. Add to creamed mixture; mix just till blended. Spread in a greased 9x9x2-inch baking pan. Bake in a 375° oven for 17 to 20 minutes. Remove. Spread with Caramel Topping: In a small saucepan combine packed brown sugar, margarine, and water. Bring to a boil, stirring constantly. Remove from heat; stir in vanilla. Gradually stir in sifted powdered sugar, adding a few drops of hot water if mixture is too thick. Stir in coconut and chopped pecans. Cool cookies and cut into bars. Makes 2 dozen bars.

Day 363

Romantic French Memory Board

Materials:
Sturdy cardboard, cut into large 24" x 24" heart shape
Paint, several colors
Foam sponge shapes
Roll of ribbon, at least 1/2" wide
Clear tape
Masking tape

Directions: Decorate the cardboard heart using the foam sponge shapes and several different colors of paint. After the paint dries, wind the ribbon randomly around the front and back of the heart, slide it into one of the notches to secure it in place. Use clear tape to secure the ribbon on the back of the cardboard. Write a special message to the recipient of the memory board (your mom? Grandmother?) and tuck it inside the ribbon on the board. Tape a loop of ribbon to the back of the board using masking tape. This gives the recipient a way to hang the memory boards.

Day 364

Box of Sayings

Materials: Index Cards
Index Card Box
Pen or Marker

Directions: Whenever you come across a saying that you think is funny or motivates you, or means something to you; write it down on an index card and put it into your special box of sayings. Over time, you will find that you will have a treasure box of sayings that are meaningful to you.

Day 365

A Gifted Girls Party

Directions: Invite your friends to the party dressed as their favorite Gifted Girls character. If they dress as Lucy, then they will have to bring their favorite clothing to the party. If they dress as Emily, then they will have to bring a picture or painting. If they dress as Daniella, then they will have to bring a dish of food. If they dress as Jackie, then they will have to bring either a natural object or something scientific. If they dress as Rose, then they will have to bring a musical instrument, music tape, movie, or something entertaining. If they have a doll of their favorite Gifted Girls character, they should bring the doll. Then have everyone discuss and share their objects and why they choose their object to represent their favorite Gifted Girls characters.

The Gifted Girls® Series

Don't miss any of the Gifted Girls® Adventures!
Ask your bookseller for a copy today or...

Order or Reserve Your Own Copy Today by Mail
or on the internet at: http://www.sparklesoup.com

Lucy and the Liberty Quilt: Book 1	$7.95 each
Lucy and the Beauty Queen: Book 2	$6.95 each
Lucy Lee Doll	$19.99 each
Emily Cobbs and The Naked Painting: Book 1	$6.95 each

Meet Emily Cobbs, a Gifted Girl from
turn-of-the-century (20th Century) England,
who has a gift with the brush.

Emily Cobbs and The Secret School: Book 2	$6.95 each

SPARKLESOUP STUDIOS, INC.
P.O. Box 142003, Irving, TX 75014

Please send me the books I have checked above. I am enclosing
$_____ (please add $3.50 to cover shipping and handling).
Send check or money order - no cash or C.O.D.'s please.

Name_____

Address_____

City_____State/Zip_____

Email Address_____

Please allow four to six weeks for delivery.

Join the Gifted Girls® Club!

Sign up at: http://www.giftedgirls.net

Find out interesting trivia about each Gifted Girl, learn about the people, places and times in history a Gifted Girl visits. Be the first to receive the latest Gifted Girls® books, jewelry, gifts, dolls, and fun fashion accessories!

Tell your friends about Gifted Girls® and start a Gifted Girls® Group where you can read books, perform fun activities, and more!